Sara Demaine was young, beautiful, on the verge of a brilliant career, and in love with Clyde Montgomery and looking forward to marrying him. Yet a year later each of them was married to someone else and Sara's career was over. What had gone wrong?

Books you will enjoy
by ROSEMARY CARTER

SAFARI ENCOUNTER

Very much against her inclination Jenny had had to accept that she couldn't go on running her father's game park alone; that she would have to let the forceful Joshua Adams virtually take over. But Jenny's real problems began when Joshua took over her heart as well!

FACE IN THE PORTRAIT

Now that, after three years, she had met Jason Peel again, Cindy knew that at all costs she must keep from him the fact that her little boy Jeremy was his son; after all the heartbreak she had been through she didn't want anything to do with Jason, ever. But Jason, she soon found, was not to be got rid of as easily as that...

DESERT DREAM

The only way Corey could get herself on to Fraser Mallory's expedition into the Kalahari Desert was to disguise herself as a man—but she really couldn't expect her disguise to remain undetected for long; nor was it. But the subsequent problems that faced her were quite different from the ones she had expected!

KELLY'S MAN

It was Kelly's fiancé's fault, not hers, that George Anderson had been injured—but it was Kelly who was doing her best to make amends, helping George's wife to go on running their hotel in the Drakensberg mountains. How galling, then, after all her efforts, that Nicholas Van Mijden should persist in thinking of her as just a spoiled rich girl!

ANOTHER LIFE

BY
ROSEMARY CARTER

MILLS & BOON LIMITED
15–16 BROOK'S MEWS
LONDON W1A 1DR

First published 1981
Australian copyright 1981
Philippine copyright 1981
This edition 1981

© *Rosemary Carter 1981*

ISBN 0 263 73573 7

Set in Monophoto Times 11 on 11½ pt.

Made and printed in Great Britain by
Richard Clay (The Chaucer Press) Ltd,
Bungay, Suffolk

CHAPTER ONE

CAPE TOWN was in the grip of wind. South-easters are always winds to respect, but this one seemed to rage with unusual fury. The waters of False Bay were swirling walls of foam. Table Mountain was invisible, the mist that normally covered its summit now a mass of grey cloud that swathed down the slopes to envelop the city.

The small red car making its way along the winding coastal road was kept on course only by the firm handling of its driver. More than once the little vehicle caught the buffet of an angry gust, giving Sara Demaine some anxious moments. As her destination came into sight she said a silent prayer of thanks. For more than one reason she was glad to glimpse the haven of her fiancé's home.

Ballet class had seemed never-ending today. Madame Olga had been more demanding than usual, her mood affected perhaps by the weather. Even less emotional people than the company's volatile teacher were made fractious by the 'Cape Doctor'.

Leaving the car, Sara made her way to the front of the building that was built into the rocky face of Clifton. The wind caught her as she rounded the corner, and for a moment she swayed with its motion, a slender figure looking almost too frail to meet the arduous demands of her profession.

Putting out a swift hand to the stone-slabbed wall, she held her balance and waited till the worst of the gust had abated. If Clifton was one of the city's most spectacular suburbs with regard to view, its exposed seashore position must also make it one of the windiest, Sara reflected ruefully. Which was why Clyde loved it so much, perhaps. With his streak of adventure and devil-may-care—an odd combination of elements in a dedicated doctor— her fiancé was rather like the wind himself, she often thought.

Almost as she rang the bell the door of the apartment opened. He had been waiting for her. He was a tall man, lean and supple, the sharp intelligence in his eyes contrasting with the hint of passion in the shape of his mouth. He was laughing as he drew her inside.

'You look like a small wind-ruffled sparrow!'

'More like a wind-ruffled and rather hassled dancer.' She threw a glance through the big picture window at the boiling sea. 'I'll never know why you choose to live in this wind-blown spot.'

'Because I love the view and the sense of free-dom. Just as I love you, my small indignant dar-ling.' She heard the bubble of laughter, husky and seductive. 'And don't pretend to pout. You know you love it as much as I do.'

The downward curve of her lips relaxed as she responded to his teasing. It was impossible for her to remain cynical in Clyde's company. Not when her senses reacted to him with a passion and an elation she had hitherto experienced only in her dancing. She had never met anyone like Clyde, she thought. She never would again. Not that she wanted to. In just three weeks they would be married, and they would be together always, sharing all the joys and the sorrows that life would bring.

His hands were at her hair, loosening the glossy dark coil from its confining knot. At his touch she felt the ignition of a flame that was becoming rapidly familiar.

'What are you doing?' she asked breathlessly.

'Turning the ballet dancer I respect into the girl I adore.'

'I thought we were going out for something to eat.' The protest in her voice was only a weak token. Her sudden hunger was not for food.

'We are, little kitten. I just want to kiss you first. And get a little warmth into those shivering bones.'

Yes, hold me. Never stop holding me. Her hands had edged beneath the unbuttoned shirt, palms flat between his body and hers as he held her close. She had never dreamed that love could be like this. That all else would pale to insignificance. Even her career, which, until the night the tall doctor with the shock of fair hair and the steel blue eyes had appeared to pay homage in her dressing-room, had been more important than anything else.

He was drawing the corduroy jacket from her shoulders. 'Don't you have anything warmer?'

'My winter coat. I didn't think it was warranted today.'

He began to plant a trail of kisses from the lobe of one ear down the sensitive column of the slender throat. In between kisses his words emerged singly. 'When I'm rich and famous you'll have furs.'

'I don't want furs.' His lips and tongue were doing intoxicating things to her nerve-stream. It was becoming increasingly hard to answer him rationally.

'I want you to have them.'

Sara was caught by the note of seriousness in his tone. Pushing herself a little away from him, she looked up. 'I don't need furs. I don't need you to be rich and famous, Clyde.'

'I need it, darling.' The words emerged with quiet emphasis.

It was not the first time he had mentioned his ambitions. He meant to achieve great things, he had told her. The ordinary run-of-the mill routine of a family doctor would not be enough for him.

'It means so much to you?' she asked him now, a little curiously.

'It does.'

The jacket was a crumpled heap on the floor. His fingers were at the buttons of her silk shirtwaist blouse. She made no effort to stop their movement.

'You should understand,' he was saying. 'You know how much your own career means to you.'

Odd how their minds could function on two levels; the intellectual one occupied with discussion of professional ideals and aspirations, the more primitive, earthy one concerned only with the need to touch and feel and be close.

'I do understand,' she said, and forbore to tell him that her own priorities had undergone a change since she had met him. Once the need to be a ballerina had been paramount. Dancing would always be important to her, she knew that with certainty. But it was no longer the most meaningful aspect of her life. Loving Clyde as she did, a new dimension had been added, one which was greater than anything she had ever imagined.

Now was not the time to tell him her feelings. For the moment her verbal responses could only be brief. They had all their lives in which to talk. Now the responses of her body were such that lucid thought was not possible.

It was apparent that Clyde's own feelings were similar. He did not refer to his ambitions again as he drew the shirt from her shoulders and undid the clasp of her bra. The small wisp of lace dropped to the floor. He stood away from her for a long moment. Sara looked up, her eyes luminous and unashamed beneath the unconcealed worship in his gaze.

'My God, you're lovely!' The words emerged on a groan. 'Sara darling, I love you so much.'

'I love you too,' she whispered.

And then they were in each other's arms, naturally, tempestuously, neither knowing who had made the first move, not caring, consumed only with the longing to be as close as possible. Sara was aware of the beat of her heart, no less rapid than when she was expending all her energies in her dancing. Somewhere near her mouth she could feel the strong pounding of Clyde's own heart, and she knew that he wanted her as much as she wanted him. Against her bare breasts she felt the smooth fabric of his shirt, and through it the warmth of his body. The top buttons were open, and without thinking she pressed her lips against the clean male-smelling skin.

She felt the tightening of his muscles as his own need deepened. With a groan he lifted her from the floor, as easily as if he had spent hours practising how to do so. With their faces on the same level, her mouth met his eagerly, her lips opening willingly to his. Her body arched towards his in an instinctive movement, born purely of the wish to be part of him.

His mouth lifted from hers, and he stared down at her still without lowering her to the ground. She could see his jaw, long and hard and with a tiny muscle working beneath it, and the heightened colour in the high-boned cheeks. She could not see his eyes, but she had no need to. She could feel her own longing repeated in him and knew what the expression would be.

'I want you, darling.' His breath was warm and clean against her face, and she could hear the husky throb in his voice. 'Sara, my darling, I don't think I can stop.'

Despite the warmth of his arms around her, she was trembling. 'I don't want you to stop.'

She heard his indrawn hiss of breath. 'We thought we'd wait. . . .'

'I know. . . .' Passion had flared between them like a raw flame many times in these last weeks, but each time they had managed to control it. They would wait until they were married, they had promised themselves. It was a promise which no longer seemed as important as it had been at the beginning. In three weeks they would be married. Sara loved Clyde more with each day, more than she had ever dreamed possible. Loved him with her mind and with her body. She could not love

him more when the ceremonious words had been
spoken and the wedding ring was on her finger.

'Let's not wait,' she whispered.

No other words were necessary. He understood
how she felt; would always understand. She did
not need to tell him why she had wanted to wait,
nor why she had changed her mind. Perhaps, she
thought, when two people loved each other their
communication went beyond words.

The blood was singing in her veins as Clyde
carried her from the living-room to the bedroom.
As a dancer she was accustomed to being held by
men, yet never before had she experienced a similar
reaction. With her dancing partners there were only
the concerns of precision and timing coupled with
a grace that made the motions seem effortless. With
Clyde there was the exhilaration of being a woman
in the arms of the man she loved.

Still without speaking he laid her down on the
bed. The look of worship did not leave his eyes as
he removed the rest of her clothes, then proceeded
to undress himself. Her throat was very full as she
watched him. His leanness was deceptive, she
thought, taking in every inch of the powerful body,
the tanned torso, the taut legs, the long arms
tapering to sensitive hands and fingers. He was
totally masculine, and with it surprisingly sensual.

And then he was lowering himself on to the bed,
and this time as he kissed her there was a fresh
depth of passion as well as a new gentleness. As if
he understood that through her longing and her
willing surrender there might be fear, he was gentle.
The long fingers began a slow caressing movement,
light and tantalising and so seductive that new fire

flamed her nerve-stream. The mobile lips traced a path down the slender column of her throat towards the small perfectly-shaped breasts, playing with each nipple in turn, letting them harden in response. Each touch set off small explosions of reaction. She hardly knew what she was doing when she reached for him, blindly, knotting her hands in the fair hair, pulling his head against her with a tiny moan.

He lay against her for a long moment, then pushed away. She met his gaze as he looked down at her and she knew that the moment of final surrender had come. She did not shift her eyes as he lowered himself against her once more. There was no fear left now. Nothing but an intense and utter happiness.

'You are quite crazy?'

Sara forced a smile at the question—no easy feat when Madame Olga's brow was puckered in an incredulous frown, and when the statement which had preceded the question was one she had desired a long time.

'No.' Her voice was unsteady. 'I mean it.'

'Any dancer worth her salt would snap at the chance of dancing Odette–Odile in *Swan Lake*. And you say no—just like that! No, Madame.'

Sara's fragile smile vanished before the onslaught. Only with difficulty could she sustain the aristocratic gaze. 'I'm getting married, Madame. . . .'

'Pouff! You'd give up *Swan Lake* for a man?'

Two months ago, Sara thought, she'd have almost been ready to trade her soul for the opportunity the ballet teacher had just offered her. She had worked very hard for just such a chance. Vivid in her memory were the hours of practice, arduous, sometimes agonising, all in the hope that one day she would rise from the corps de ballet. But two months ago there had been no Clyde in her life. Had she been told that she would throw up the chance of a lifetime for the love of a man she would have laughed.

'You don't understand, Madame.' Her chin lifted. She did not know that the watching teacher saw through the challenge to the hint of sadness that lay beneath. 'I'm very honoured by the offer. But I love Clyde. I. . . . I have to put him first.'

'I understand that you are in love,' Madame Olga said, more gently now. Glancing at the proud chiselled face of the teacher, Sara had an intimation of the beauty she must once have been. 'At least, you think you are. And for that you forgo all that you have worked for.' She paused, and the smallest sign of softening appeared at the corners of her painted lips. 'For a few days I keep the offer open. Think, Sara. Perhaps you will come to your senses.'

And that was the one thing that would not happen, Sara knew as she negotiated the small red car along the mountain road an hour later. She had set her life upon a new course. Not even the temptation of dancing *Swan Lake* could alter it. There was a time when she had thought nothing could come between her and her career. When the lure of being a ballerina had been the spur that had kept up her enthusiasm when the rigorous demands of the dance might have broken her spirit.

It had been her dream, her total life ambition. It had been the all-important priority. All other considerations had had to be slotted around it or be discarded.

Clyde's entry into her life had been unexpected, his impact as dramatic as a streak of lightning in a cloudless sky. And with the same unexpectedness her world had changed. The dream which had hitherto been all-encompassing had been displaced by a new dream. Not that the old dream had vanished. Dancing would always be important to her, Sara knew. But it was no longer her top priority. Marriage and plans for a shared life had that place now. Dancing could only be on the periphery.

Which was why she had refused the offer to dance *Swan Lake*. She would continue to work in the city, as opportunities presented themselves. Clyde would not mind if she danced, at least until they began a family. But the company would be touring the country with *Swan Lake*, entailing weeks away from home. Sara's answer had needed little thought. The pangs of refusal—useless to deny that she had experienced some—were meaningless against the idea of separation from Clyde.

Glancing at her watch, she saw that she was early for the lunch at the home of Clyde's parents. It would be one of several affairs to be held in anticipation of the wedding, her fiancé had told her with a grimace. He would be coming straight from the hospital and would meet her at the house.

After the discussion with Madame Olga, Sara had been a little dispirited. She felt better as she drove more slowly along the winding mountain road. Today the weather was glorious, one of those perfect Cape days when the sky was cloudless and the summit of Table Mountain was a finely etched line against the blue. The sea was a deep aquamarine with small sailing craft skimming the waves. Silver trees and proteas grew at the roadside. Winding down the window, Sara took long breaths of the spicy air, and felt the depression of inevitable disappointment lifting.

Just a little more than two weeks and she and Clyde would be man and wife. The apartment high on the windy stone face of Clifton would be home. There would be days of busy activity, nights of love and shared dreams.

A luminous look came into eyes that were green and vivid against the dark glossy frame of her hair. The night in Clyde's apartment was never far from her thoughts. She had not slept with him again since then, for later, when they had made a meal of cheese and wine and crusty bread, they had decided to keep a rein on their emotions until the wedding was over. Yet she did not regret what had happened. There had been pain, yes, but there had also been a bursting of emotion and a beauty she could not have imagined. Afterwards, in Clyde's manner had been a new tenderness. For her own part, she had been swept with a surge of love that went beyond anything she had felt before.

Reaching the house, Sara saw that several cars were parked in the drive, but Clyde's was not one of them. No doubt he had been delayed at the hospital. In the kitchen, her future mother-in-law confirmed the thought. Giving Sara a quick hug, she declined her offer of help; she could cope best if she worked alone, she said, then added, 'The rest of the family are in the garden. Why don't you join them?'

Unhurriedly Sara strolled through the trees. She had met several members of Clyde's family, and was looking forward to knowing them better, but the last days had been tiring, and she was enjoying the warmth of the sun on her skin, the feel of the soft grass beneath her feet.

Set against a forested slope, the house was particularly lovely with its gracefully curving Cape Dutch gables, and the splashes of scarlet bougainvillaea against the pristine white of its walls. The windows were mullioned, the glass aflame with golden shafts of sun, and from the big carved wooden door, wide stone steps led on to a carpet-smooth lawn. Bushes and shrubs were everywhere; mainly the indigenous plants of the Cape Peninsula. There were aloes and proteas, their waxy flowers making a spectacular display. There was a clump of strelitzia, the strange yellow flowers shaped like exotic birds poised for flight. There were the rockflowers, mesembreanthemums of deep purple, and daisies of every size and colour.

In a small arbour she saw a bench and sat down. Nearby was an ornamental pool, and a kingfisher dipped and soared above the water. Dancer that she was, Sara was enchanted by the grace of the bird's fluid movements.

She did not know when she became aware of the voices. Perhaps it was only at the sound of her name that she jerked up. Two women were talking, and she recognised the one voice, not the other. Belinda, Clyde's sister, was talking to a woman a little older than herself. Sara's first instinct was to join them, then, as she was caught by something in the voices, she remained where she was.

'. . . .and with Sara he may never get there, I suppose,' the stranger was saying.

'Not in the foreseeable future, Mary,' Belinda agreed.

'What a damned shame!' Mary was indignant. 'Clyde was always outstanding. He'd have made a fantastic surgeon. As a family doctor he'll be wasted.'

'Not wasted, perhaps. But he won't be fulfilling his potential.' There was a pause. Then Belinda said, 'As long as I can remember, my brother has wanted to be a surgeon. This . . . this marriage has just shattered us all.'

From the start Sara had registered a certain coldness in Belinda's attitude. It was something Clyde had dismissed when she had mentioned it. She was too sensitive, he had said, so that she made too much of vibrations. His sister, older than himself and unmarried, had always inclined towards protectiveness; a slight suspicion of any woman he might choose to marry was only natural. With a longer acquaintance Belinda's stiffness would vanish. Wanting to believe him, Sara had not pursued the subject.

'Have you talked to him?' Mary wanted to know.

'Once or twice, with no success.' The bitterness in Belinda's tone deepened. 'He's completely infatuated with the girl.'

'How did she catch him?'

Catch him. . . . Sara cherished the memory of the day in the dressing-room, when Clyde had appeared to tell her how much he had enjoyed her dancing. Every moment of the scene was as clearly engraved on her mind as if it had just taken place. There had been the fatigue and exhilaration which followed the strain of the performance. Then the shock, disbelief almost, at first sight of the tall lean stranger with the chiselled features and the piercing blue eyes. The feeling, insane perhaps and ridiculous, that he was above all other men she knew, that she would never meet another like him. The tingling as he had taken her hand and kissed it in a gesture of homage that seemed to belong to another age. The certainty that if she never saw him again she would nevertheless never forget him.

And then the wonder when it became clear that his own feelings were very similar to her own. The wonder of knowing that her own impact on Clyde had been as great as his had been on her.

Catch him. . . . Even when she had understood what was happening to her, she had been stubborn. They could be friends, she had told him almost despairingly, when he had proposed marriage for the fourth time. She could still remember his answer.

'I'm a man, Sara, a normal man with normal needs. I want you—as a wife, not as a friend, not even as a mistress. I want to come home to you every evening, to reach for you in the night. . . .'

There had been a hardness in his tone, so that she had recognised the ultimatum for what it was. Either she married him or she would not see him again. And with it had come the recognition of her own feelings, so that she knew that in loving Clyde she had discovered a meaning in life that transcended the importance of the dance.

That moment had been precious. She did not want it cheapened by the words spoken by Belinda and her friend. Blindly she looked around her, searching for a way of escape, a means of getting out of earshot. If there was more to the conversation she did not want to hear it. But she was trapped. The only way out of the arbour was past the two women. She could not take that way without revealing that she had listened to them talk.

'It wasn't difficult to catch him,' she heard Belinda say. 'Clyde was on the rebound. He was just beginning to accept that Andrea had taken up with someone else.'

Pain stabbed at Sara, sharp and unexpected. The name had been dropped so casually into the conversation. Clyde had never spoken of an Andrea, had never even hinted at the existence of a previous relationship. Yet Belinda's mention was so matter-of-fact as to leave no doubt that such a relationship must have been very real.

Don't say any more, she pleaded silently. Don't destroy something that's been so beautiful. Unbidden came the memory of the night in Clyde's arms, when for a while there had been no meaning except the expression of love between two rapturous bodies. Don't say any more. . . .

'Andrea Stanford?' Mary asked curiously. 'Professor Stanford's daughter? Was Clyde serious about her?'

'Very much so. Now there's a marriage that would have benefited him. A man in the Professor's position. . . . Clyde could only have progressed.'

'And yet. . . .' there was a thoughtfulness in

Mary's tone, 'if Clyde is serious about becoming a surgeon, perhaps this marriage won't affect him.'

'It can hardly do otherwise. He'll have to devote himself to making a living, providing all the fripperies a girl like that will want. Andrea's father would have made it possible for him to further his studies. With Sara life will just become the drudgery of a family doctor's existence.'

'She's a pretty little thing,' Mary offered. 'I've seen her dance. I can understand why he fell in love with her.'

'Love!' Belinda's contempt was sharp. 'All Clyde feels is infatuation. When he wakes up and realises what his little dancer has made of his life he'll start to hate her.'

'Surely it's not too late to talk to him. God, Belinda, it's hot here, can't we find some shade? And I'd like a cool drink. . . .'

They were moving away now, their voices becoming an indistinguishable blur, their words lost. Sara could leave the arbour now. Nobody would see her.

But she made no effort to move. It was as hot as Mary had said. Even here, where the tracery of creepers provided shade of a sort, the sun shafted through in burning rays. Yet Sara felt cold, a numbing coldness that came from inside.

Much of what Belinda had said could well stem from simple dislike, a clash of different personalities. But it was impossible to dismiss everything. Clyde had been alone at the ballet, a strange situation now that Sara considered it for the first time. A man as good-looking as Clyde Montgomery would not have to look far for beautiful women to accompany him. Perhaps after his recent break with the woman he had intended marrying, the thought of another date had been abhorrent. And with the abhorrence there could yet have been the unconscious wish for a new relationship, the wish to show Andrea that she had not hurt him as much as she imagined. People did find new partners on the rebound, Sara knew.

The more she thought about it, the more likely it seemed that this was what had in fact happened. Men like Clyde did not normally fall in love as quickly as he had done.

Something else Belinda had said was true. Clyde was ambitious. He himself had told her that riches and fame meant much to him. She knew that he had thought of specialising in surgery, but had gathered that he planned to do so some time in the future, when he had set aside enough to withdraw from practice for a few years. She had not dreamed that his plans had been so immediate, that only their marriage had put a stop to them. He had not talked much about his plans, just as he had not talked about Andrea Stanford. Perhaps he had been tactful. Sara wished he would rather have been honest.

He would grow to hate her, Belinda had said. The first flush of infatuation would fade, and there would be no lasting love to sustain it. It was then that he would grow to resent his wife for the career he had forgone and which meant so much to him. Perhaps he would even grow to hate her—and Sara knew that she loved him too much to endure that.

She had to talk to him, had to tell him that she would not marry him, had to find a way of telling

him in a way that would not let him persuade her
otherwise; for if he knew her reasons for backing
down he would dispel them and insist on the marriage. Later he would regret it.

She had to talk to him, as soon as possible. The
wedding was only just over two weeks away.
Emerging from the arbour, she saw the gabled
house, and stopped short. The party! Already
people were gathered on the lawn just below the
stone steps.

She could not go to the party, could not talk to
the many people who had come to meet the bride.
She could not smile and play the part of a girl
excited and in love. A certain amount of pretence
lay before her, that much she knew, but she also
knew that there were limits to how much she could
tolerate.

There were more cars on the drive now, she saw
as she approached the house, but Clyde's was not
one of them. If she moved quickly she might
manage to leave here before he arrived. He would
be angry that she had given him the slip, especially
when he found out the reason, but his anger was
something she would have to face. It would be
easier to contend with than the part of the radiant
bride.

Clyde's mother was disappointed when Sara told
her she could not stay. She had a dreadful head-
ache, she said, felt as if she was coming down with
'flu. Clyde would look after her, said his mother,
she should lie down in one of the bedrooms and
when he came he would prescribe some medicine.

Sara was adamant. She was sorry to leave the
party, especially when it was being given in her

honour, but she felt that the only place for her was home. She was glad that she did not see Belinda on her way to the car. If that girl had said she was sorry Sara was leaving, she might well have countered with something she would later regret.

CHAPTER TWO

THE knock at the door came less than an hour later, and Sara did not have to wonder who was there. She took a deep breath for courage as she crossed the room.

'Sara darling, what's wrong?' Clyde's face was creased in concern as he strode into the room. And then, as he looked down at her, his expression altered. 'Mother said you were ill, but you don't look it.'

Sara swallowed. 'I'm not.'

The frown deepened. 'Then why did you leave the party?'

'Clyde. . . .' She choked on the name.

'Darling, what's wrong?' He had closed the gap between them and she saw that he meant to draw her to him. She took a step away.

'Sara! You're very white. Darling, what is it?'

It was very hard to maintain her composure. He was no more than inches from her, and despite her decision to break with him, she was swept with the desire to be in the haven of his arms. He looked so tall, so virile. There was no way she could prevent her senses responding to him. It took every bit of self-control she possessed to maintain her composure when with every nerve and fibre she ached to fling herself against him and to beg him for reassurance that Belinda's assertions had not been true.

'We have to talk.' Her voice was very low.

A muscle tightened in the long line of the jaw. 'I don't think I like the sound of that.'

'Sit down, Clyde,' she said quietly.

His eyes narrowed. They could be warm as the sky on a sunny day, but now they held a touch of steel. As if he sensed what was coming, Sara thought.

He walked to the two-seater couch. 'All right then, let's sit.' From his attitude it was clear that he intended her to join him.

She went instead to one of the cane chairs by the window. Strange how hard it was to give her feet purpose. Normally her legs were like finely-tuned precision instruments, conditioned to responding to the slightest direction, but at this moment they felt as insubstantial as water.

'Sara darling,' Clyde's voice was unexpectedly gentle, 'I've never seen you look so miserable. Whatever it is that's worrying you, it can't be as bad as you think it is.' He leaned forward, his arms long enough to reach to her from the couch, and as he took her hands in his she felt the familiar quickening in her bloodstream. It came to her that it would be well-nigh impossible to get Clyde out of her system.

She tried to withdraw her hands from his, for the contact only made it more difficult to say what she had to—but failed. His hold was deceptively light. He was not making it easy for her.

The blue eyes held hers, steady, too perceptive. Sara let her own eyes slide from his gaze. She swallowed hard, then said, with all the conviction she could muster, 'I can't marry you.'

'What!' The word was an explosion. The grip on

her hands tightened as his fingers grew rigid. The fragile hands of the dancer felt bruised, but now she made no move to escape him. 'Say that again!' His tone was savage.

Tears had gathered behind her lids, and at the back of her throat a lump had formed. Keeping as tight a rein as she could on her emotions—it would make nonsense of her statement if she were to let herself cry—she said once more, 'I can't marry you.'

There was a moment of silence, a silence that was almost tangible in its intensity. Sara did not let herself glance at Clyde. To do so could well be her undoing.

Then he said softly, 'Look at me.'

Blindly she shook her head. 'I. . . . Don't make it harder.'

'I'll make it as hard as I damn well wish!'

She grew rigid as one hand left hers and caught her chin. He drew her round to face him. Short of closing her eyes there was no way of escaping his gaze.

'Now,' Clyde said very softly, 'say it again.'

He was very near her. Through the threatening tears she could see every line and crevice of the chiselled face; the furrows that curved from the edge of his nostrils to the corners of his mouth, the firmness of the jaw and chin, the bushiness of eyebrows that were as fair as his hair, and the eyes, those wonderfully intelligent eyes that could warm with laughter and love and tenderness and which were now alight with an alarming perception, as if he could see right through to the thoughts inside her. She could feel his power and virility communicated through the touch of his fingers, a touch which inevitably brought to mind all the moments she had spent in his arms. She could smell the maleness of him, so that briefly she felt quite dizzy.

For a moment she was tempted to go back on her words. Let Belinda Montgomery think what she liked about the ballet dancer her brother wanted to marry! It did not matter what she thought. All that mattered was that Sara loved Clyde, that he loved her, that she would never know a similar love. Spiteful words should not have the power to ruin two lives.

But a small voice told her that what Belinda had said did matter. Clyde's sister could not have known of the eavesdropper in the arbour. She had only stated the situation as she saw it. And while Sara longed to disbelieve what she had heard, that part of her which was still rational knew it was true.

'Sara. . . .' Clyde was so close to her that she could feel his breath fanning her cheek.

Heedless of the tears that now trembled on her lashes, she met his gaze as steadily as she could. 'I can't marry you. You must accept it.'

She heard him take a breath. 'Why?'

He would not believe her if she said she did not love him. Her tears, her obvious distress, were enough to refute the truth of the words. As if in answer to her thoughts, he said, 'Don't tell me your feelings have changed.'

She shook her head. The solution came suddenly, so that she wondered why she had not thought of it before. As a dancer she needed exquisite control. She had not known she was capable of the control she summoned now.

Her voice was only slightly unsteady as she said, 'I've had an offer. The company wants me to dance *Swan Lake*.'

The expression in the blue eyes altered fractionally, as if he wondered how the news could affect him.

'Congratulations. It's what you've always wanted.'

'That's right. And that's why . . .' she dug her nails into the soft palms so hard that they hurt, 'I've decided to accept the offer.'

Clyde shot her a look that was long and level. 'That's fine with me.'

'We'll be going on tour. We could be away a long time. . . .'

His eyes were narrowed, watchful. 'That does change things. The purpose of marriage is to be together.'

'That's why. . . . Clyde, you have to understand.' She was unaware of the pleading in her tone.

'You could decline *Swan Lake*. There'll be other roles, opportunities to dance in the city.'

'No!' The wildness of despair was in the exclamation. 'I'm a ballet dancer, with all it entails— touring, the lot.'

'And you're saying your career means more to you than marriage?'

'Yes.' The word emerged on a half-sob.

Silence followed the affirmation, a silence more total than the earlier one. Clyde's face had grown very pale, the skin as taut over the gaunt cheekbones as if drawn over a mask. The blue eyes had never been quite so cold. For what seemed a long time he sat very still, his gaze never leaving her face. Sara thought later that during those moments she did not breathe.

'I'm wondering,' he said at last, in a voice that was totally without expression, 'why you chose this particular time to make your decision. The night we slept together'—the words came out deliberately, as if he enjoyed seeing her flinch—'you couldn't wait for us to be married. Why now, Sara?'

'Clyde. . . .'

'What happened at the party? Mother said you were fine when you got to the house, that you came in suddenly and said you weren't feeling well. Obviously that wasn't true.'

'No. . . .' She tried to hold his gaze. She could not tell him the truth, but she did owe him co-operation.

'What happened at the party, Sara?' he asked.

'The party had nothing to do with it. Not in itself. . . .' Her voice was very low. She wondered if he heard her despair. 'This morning . . . Madame Olga offered me the part. It . . . well, it was un-expected. I was so excited. . . .' She stopped, fighting for control. 'I didn't give her an answer. There was the party . . . and I had to see you.' The words were coming more easily now. She lifted her chin in an attempt to show confidence. 'You weren't there when I came. I walked in the garden, and I did some thinking. And . . . and I realised how much ballet means to me. I can't give it up, Clyde, not even for you.' The last sentence emerged on a husky whisper.

She waited for him to answer, but he did not. She found the silence unnerving. The air between

them was thick with a tension more intense than
anything she had ever experienced, more intense
even than the strain backstage on the first night of
a new ballet. Clyde's mouth, always firm, had
become an inflexible line, in his eyes was a glint
that was infinitely dangerous.

Sara tried to swallow. 'Say something,' she said
at last.

'Say something,' he mocked her. 'Say what, my
darling fiancée? That I condone what you're doing
to us? That I forgive you for the havoc you've
created in my life?'

'Just . . . that you understand,' she pleaded.

He laughed shortly, without any humour. 'You
want a lot, don't you, Sara? Yes, my dear, there
are things that I understand. For one, that your
career means more to you than I do.'

Nothing in the world means more to me than
you do. If I had to choose between my career and
you, my darling, my love, the choice would be you
every time.

Aloud she said, 'Yes.'

The eyes that were colder and harder than she
had ever imagined they could be, swept the fragile
body with a gaze that was deliberately insulting. 'I
also understand that you enjoyed my lovemaking.
I thought it was the first time for you. Now I
wonder how many other men you've had.'

'None! I was a virgin.' She threw the words at
him vehemently. Seconds later she realised that the
shrewder tactic might have been to concede the
accusation.

'A very passionate virgin,' he drawled outrageously.

She caught a soft lip between small white teeth. Was this how things ended? she wondered. With pain, and anger, and deliberate hurt? 'Do you have to be so cruel?' she asked unsteadily. 'We could still see each other. This . . . this doesn't have to be a final parting.'

His lips curled. 'You're offering to be my mistress?'

Why not? Until a few weeks ago she would have rejected the very idea out of hand. But a few weeks ago she had had no inkling of the rapture and the torment that love could bring. Principles which had been instilled in her all her life had been the ones she abided by, and she had never had reason to question them.

Now all was changed. There would never be anybody but Clyde. Even if she never saw him again she knew that she could love nobody else. That being the case, what harm in being his mistress? There would still be the love and the togetherness she craved, which he seemed to want also. There would also be freedom, at least on his part. He would be able to pursue his future without the trappings of a wife and family to hinder him.

Green eyes looked into blue ones. 'Yes, I'll be your mistress.'

'Everything on a platter, with no commitments on either side.' Clyde was smiling, but as with his laughter moments earlier, without humour. 'How very satisfying! I'd like another taste of what that holds.'

Without warning, he stood up. He was still holding one of her hands, and he yanked her up with him, his grip so hard that the slender wrist

could have snapped. She was pulled up against the
long wall of his body, but where before there had
always been tenderness in his movements, now
there was only a suggestion of force.

She managed to draw back her head just as his
own was descending. 'Not like this,' she protested,
her cheeks burning, her head pounding with pain.

'You want loving on your own terms, Sara?' His
voice was a whiplash. 'You've done all the dictating
up till now. Now it's my turn.'

There was no chance to escape as he jerked her
to him once more. No escaping the mouth that
crushed down on hers, forcing her lips apart. No
escaping the ravaging of her mouth in a kiss that
was demanding and brutal.

For a few moments his possession of her was so
forceful that she was too shaken to resist. Then, as
outrage surged within her, she tried to squeeze her
hands between them, tried to pummel at his chest.
Easily, without loosening his hold, he pushed her
hands downward, and kept them both in one of
his, while his other arm pulled against her back.

Once he lifted his head for breath and looked
down at her. The eyes that met his were big and
wet and distressed. 'Please, stop,' she whispered.

If the sight of her obvious unhappiness affected
him, there was no indication of it in his tone. 'This
is just the beginning. You made the offer, Sara.
You might as well see what you'd be letting yourself in for.'

Again the strong mouth came down, but this
time the cruelty was gone, and in its place was a
tantalising seductiveness that sent explosions of
desire flaming through her body. His arousal of

her was deliberate. In some remote part of her mind she knew that, but there was a hunger inside her that would not be denied. Her senses overruled her, letting her body act without her volition. As the mobile lips explored the sweetness of her mouth, and the long-fingered hands slid roughly beneath her dress to the bareness of her skin, she arched towards him, bringing up her hands to bury themselves in the thick hair at the back of his neck.

Her response did not escape him. She felt the hardening of his muscles, the evidence of his own passion. There was no thought in her now, no premonition of remorse. There was only a need which ached to be fulfilled.

She was pliant as he moulded her to him, unresistant when he pulled at her zip and ripped the dress from her shoulders. Her body was on fire. There was no memory of what had happened in the last hours, no rationalising of what was right and for the best. Only the longing to love him, to be part of him. . . .

When he stepped away from her and looked down at her, she met his eyes in a passion-dazed blur. It took a few seconds for her to realise that he was making no move to remove his own clothes. It took a little longer to understand that he had intended to sever the physical contact between them.

'Clyde. . . .' She took a step towards him, reached out her hands. 'Clyde, what's wrong?'

'Nothing at all, except that I've lost the taste for this.'

'You said . . . you wanted me . . . as a mistress.' She felt suddenly very ill.

'*You* made the suggestion.' His breathing was only slightly heightened. His colour was higher than it had been, but his tone was deliberately flat.

'And now . . . you're rejecting me.' The words emerged with difficulty.

This was not happening, she thought wildly. This cruel interchange between two people who until today had wanted only love and who now seemed bent on hurting each other.

'Call it what you like.' There was no mercy in the eyes that raked her half-clothed body.

Feeling suddenly embarrassed before him, she put up her hands to cover her breasts, and saw the gleam that came into his eyes. He knew just how she felt, she thought, and he was glad. He himself must have been even more hurt by her rejection than she had realised.

'You don't want me. . . .'

'As a wife, I did. You know that. As a mistress . . .' still that hateful flatness, 'thank you, but no.'

There was a pain in her chest, dull and hard. In her eyes the tears which had been threatening for the last half hour had gathered in new force. Any moment now she would cry. She longed to cry, to be released from the distress that was rapidly becoming unbearable. But she would not cry in front of Clyde. There was a time when she could have done so, secure in the fact that he would have comforted her with a love and tenderness she would find in nobody else.

That was no longer the case. Rejection had made Clyde a stranger, a hard contemptuous man with a side to his personality which she had never suspected. There was no way she could tell him of the sacrifice she had make for his sake. Nor, it seemed, was there a way in which their relationship could continue on a different basis. In the circumstances she wanted only to be alone.

'Go,' she said in a low voice. 'Just leave me alone, Clyde.'

When the door had closed behind him she threw herself on to her bed and wept with more abandon than she had done even as a child. Yet when she sat up at last, tear-stained and cold and filled with a dreadful numbness, she knew that if the tears had been a release they had nevertheless done little to make her feel better.

Sara threw herself into her dancing with a frenzy that she had not known she possessed. Odette and Odile, two such dissimilar characters, customarily danced by the same person, was a role that tested many a dancer's capabilities. In Sara's rendition, Odette, the swan-maiden, became a girl of tantalising loveliness. Her Odile, the wicked mischiefmaker, was spectacular. There was a spring in her step, an almost electric sparkle in her movement, which gave the evil character a vivacious sex appeal which drew more praise than usual in rehearsals.

Now and then Sara found Madame Olga looking at her with puzzled eyes. The ballet teacher had accepted her change of mind with satisfaction. It was as if she had known that no dancer of talent would reject such an opportunity. Yet as the rehearsals progressed, and later as the tour began, there was almost an uneasiness in the teacher's manner. It was as if she distrusted the change in her protégée. More than once she asked Sara if something was the matter, stopping just short of mentioning Clyde and the question of whether the girl regretted ending her engagement. No, Sara assured her each time, she had never felt better. Odette-Odile was the part she had been waiting for from the moment she had watched *Swan Lake* as a child, and had known she herself would one day become a ballerina.

Madame Olga was not the only one to register the change in the girl's personality. Peter Burod, choreographer of the company, a very wealthy man, and once a famous ballet dancer himself, was taken by the tiny girl with the glossy hair and the desperate fire in her sea-green eyes. He asked her to have dinner with him, a departure from his usual aloofness from the girls in the corps de ballet. Sara went with him. There was no reason not to. Since her break with Clyde one person was much like another; nobody did more than hover on the periphery of her awareness.

It was on their third evening out together that Peter asked her to marry him. He had fallen in love with her, he told her. He was much older than she was, forty-seven to her twenty-two years, but he loved her as he had not loved any other woman since the death of his wife some years earlier.

As gently as she could, Sara refused him. The weeks with Clyde had given her an added sensitivity. She had never been one to hurt people when she could avoid it, but such was her own hurt now that she could empathise with the feelings of another. She liked him very much, she told him, and was honoured by his proposal—the words in this instance not a cliché, for such was the personality of Peter Burod that a proposal from the man was indeed an honour—but she did not love him. Peter, who knew of her broken relationship (not the details, for there were none who knew those), did not press her. The offer was open. If she needed someone to lean on or confide in, he would not fail her.

The gallant kindness of the man was warming. And Sara had much need of warmth and reassurance. The first performance of *Swan Lake* was drawing near, and with it the pressures within the company were increasing. There were new demands on the dancers, doubts and fears and insecurities. There were temper tantrums and fierce differences of opinions. Nerves were stretched to breaking point.

In a sense Sara welcomed the crowded hours, the feverishness. She had little time for thought. Only at night, when she lay in bed, her body and her emotions throbbing with exhaustion, did she think of Clyde. Then the grief of the parting would wash over her with a pain that seemed never to grow less.

Just two weeks before opening night Sara learned that she was pregnant. So preoccupied had she been that she had failed to recognise symptoms which ordinarily she would not have ignored.

'You must take care of yourself.' The doctor who examined her wore an expression of concern.

'I'm a dancer. We're going on tour. . . .'

'Put it off.'

'I can't.'

He shook his head thoughtfully. 'Pregnancy is
not a state of ill health. But neither is it an endurance test. And in your case. . . .' In his eyes was
an expression of doubt, as if he sensed something
without being able to quite pinpoint its nature. 'Try
to take things easy, Miss Demaine.'

In a daze she left the medical building and made
for her car. Rehearsals had ended early for once,
which was why she had been able to take the appointment. Instead of heading back towards the
empty apartment, to rest as the doctor had advised,
she took a road that ran beside the sea. Bypassing
the beaches where holidaymakers sunbathed, she
stopped the car at length at a lonely viewpoint,
where a narrow path fell steeply to the water's
edge.

There was no beach here, just a scrambled line
of jagged rocks. Sara chose one that was smoother
than the rest, and leaned against it. During high
tide these rocks would be submerged, but even
now, when the sea was low, the waves beat cease-
lessly against the farthest stone, one wave after
another hitting the rocks with a roar and spurting
of foam.

The wildness of the scene was an appropriate
setting for Sara's tumultuous state of mind. A
baby, in less than six months. The knowledge
brought a welter of emotions and questions and
memories.

Memories more than anything else. In the weeks
since their parting, she had tried to shut from her
mind the hours in Clyde's apartment, when she had
lain in his arms and he had made love to her as a
woman. She had had no wish to dwell on the

ecstasy which had been with her then; that was an indulgence which only deepened the anguish that knifed and tore within her.

Now it was a memory which she could no longer ignore. She had to come to terms with the memory of a love she would never know again, a love which had led to very real consequences.

How naïve she had been, she thought now, that the possibility of pregnancy had never occurred to her, either at the time of the lovemaking or later. There had been only two people, caught up in the rapture of their feelings for each other. Nothing else had mattered.

What would Clyde's reaction be to this new development? she wondered. She remembered very clearly his anger on learning that she would not marry him. The violence with which he had kissed her—a violence born of anger. There had been no love in his kisses. The love he had felt for her once had been killed when he understood that her career meant more to her than he did.

And yet, even now, if Clyde were to learn the truth, he might insist on marrying her. It was part of his nature that he would want to assume responsibility for the tiny being that was as much of his flesh as it was of hers.

But Clyde would not know. She would never tell him. The decision not to marry him had been very difficult; it had also been made for a very definite reason. If Clyde would have found it difficult to further his career when he had only a wife to consider, the added encumbrance of a child would mean the end of his plans.

Sara picked up a small weather-rounded pebble

and threw it into the turbulent spray, watching as it whirled in a swathe of foam before being dragged seawards. The very fact that Clyde's child was growing inside her had created a new longing. She wanted Clyde so badly that the wanting was like a physical ache. But the wanting could never be assuaged by a forced marriage, which was what any marriage between them could only be at this point. The loveliness that had once existed between them would be supplanted by a growing and inevitable bitterness. Belinda had said so, and Sara knew it was true. No—far better to be apart from Clyde, bringing up alone the child which would be a lasting memory of their love.

There were also other problems to consider. Her career, more particularly her part in *Swan Lake*. Rest, the doctor had said; but rest was the one luxury she could not afford. Apart from the disappointment she would suffer in giving up the part of Odette–Odile, the approaching birth made finance a very real worry. Now she had been promoted to ballerina Sara would earn enough to tide her over a while. By the time her resources had dried up the baby would be a few months old and she would have regained the strength and the figure to resume dancing. Somehow she must support both her child and herself.

Thoughtfully Sara put a hand over her stomach. There was only the slightest suggestion of a curve, so slight that until today she had not noticed it; it would not show through her costumes. She was small, the doctor had said. Perhaps she would remain so. There were women who were obviously pregnant at three months; others who were able to hide the signs very much longer. She could only hope that she belonged to the latter category.

As she made her way back up the narrow path to the car she decided that nobody should know of her pregnancy. Not Clyde, not Madame Olga or Peter Burod or the members of the company. She would dance Odette-Odile to the best of her ability and for as long as she possibly could. In a few months she would consider further. She could only take her life one step at a time.

· CHAPTER THREE

BACKSTAGE the atmosphere was one of frenetic
exhilaration. Nerves were strained to breaking
point. In Sara's dressing-room there was intense
quiet. She was quite alone, a figure slender to the
point of fragility, clad in the delicate white costume
of a swan-maiden. Her hair was a glossy coil, her
face had been made up with care. Only Sara, seated
at her mirror, saw the pallor beneath the grease-
paint.

Madame Olga had been in with last-minute
words of encouragement, her usually acerbic personality softened. Peter Burod had spoken with her
too, and had given her a small pendant with a
dainty amber stone. For luck, he had said, but
Sara, who knew that other ballerinas did not re-
ceive such presents from him, had been touched.

Only from Clyde had there been no sign, no
word. Did he know she was dancing today? Sara
wondered. Yes—if he had made a point of find-
ing out. She had hoped that he would send her
flowers, a gesture of forgiveness and understanding. She had understood too that only a complete
break could be effective. As it was, there had
been nothing. In the minutes while she waited for
the first curtain call, Sara acknowledged that
despite all her rationalising, she was disappointed.

And then the moment for personal introspec-
tion was gone. She was on stage. Sara Demaine

was no longer a girl with problems that concerned only herself. She was Odette, the swan-maiden with a problem easily identifiable by an audience, many of whom had seen *Swan Lake* before, and who were as caught by this rendering as if they were seeing the dance performed for the first time.

Sara knew herself that her dancing was good. It was as if her grief and disappointment had inspired her, so that she rose above her problems and danced as she had never danced before. She felt a new spring in her steps, a grace in her arms, a sense of space and movement so fluid that there were moments when she felt as if she was flying. The vociferous applause at the end of the act revealed that the audience were caught in the spell that gripped her.

And then she was dancing Odile. If Odette epitomised all the feminine virtues, Odile was the opposite. As the daughter of the evil wizard, out to snare the handsome prince for herself, she was the embodiment of all that was bad. She was also beautiful, with a sensual zest and vitality which captured the imagination of the courtiers before whom she performed. It was a part which taxed a dancer to the fullest.

Sara was on her pointes when the pain shot through her—an agonising pain. Winded, she held the movement a beat too long, and then, as she managed to catch her breath, she was dancing again. Only the discerning eye would have picked up the fault.

Minutes later the pain came again. This time she was ready for it. Conditioning and discipline helped her to surmount it.

She was Odile still when the pain came again—
an all-encompassing pain this time. A scream rent
the air as Odile, the wicked enchantress, became
Sara, a mortal girl. The audience let out a collective
moan as she fell unconscious on the stage.

Slowly, with great effort, she opened her eyes.
Dizziness, a dreadful dizziness, was all she registered at first—a strange lethargy that seemed to
have gripped her limbs, a feeling of total un-
reality.

Whiteness. All around her an unfocussed whiteness. Dimly the image of music, of movement. . . .
And then memory flooded back, and she was trying
to focus her vision, to make some sense of the
sterile quietness of her surroundings. She tried to
sit up.

A hand restrained her, pushing her gently back
against the pillows. 'Rest, Sara. . . .'

A voice she knew. She frowned, tried to focus
once more, and saw the face of Peter Burod.

'Peter . . .?' Her voice was low with bewilder-
ment.

'Hush, my dear.'

'The performance. . . .'

'You were taken ill.' He spoke gently, his voice
drifting over her like a caress. 'You're in hospital,
Sara.'

'Odile. . . .' She was trying to make some sense
of the images that merged one into another. 'I was
dancing Odile. . . .'

'You were taken ill,' he said again.

'I must go back.' Distress in her voice as she

tried to struggle up once more.

'You must rest.' He eased her back. 'Don't worry about the ballet, Sara. Maria took over . . . your understudy . . .'

No! Maria can't dance Odette–Odile. My part, the one I worked for. *My* part!

'No!' she said aloud, with a violence at odds with her weakness.

A nurse appeared beside the bed with a glass of water and a pill.

'I don't want this,' Sara protested.

'You have to have it, honey. We want to save your baby.'

Sara's eyes flew to Peter. His expression was un-changed—grave, concerned, understanding.

'You know?' she asked softly, when the nurse had gone.

'Yes.'

'I'm so sorry. . . .' she whispered.

'For what?' he asked, a little roughly. 'Because you're human?'

'Because I ruined the performance.'

'Don't worry about that.' He took her hand. 'Why didn't you say anything?'

'I . . . I couldn't. I . . . I wanted to go on dancing . . . for as long as possible. . . .'

'There was a doctor here, Sara, while you were unconscious. He said you'd been told to rest.'

'Yes.'

'Sara, who is Clyde?' asked Peter.

She felt something tighten inside her. 'Clyde is here?' she whispered.

'No, Sara.' He stroked her hand gently, and she saw the compassion in his eyes. 'But you spoke of him, called for him.'

'I see.' Her voice was dull.

'Wasn't Clyde the man you were engaged to?'

'Yes . . .'

'And he's the father of your baby?'

'Yes.'

'Clyde who? I'll phone him. He should be with you.'

'No!' Nerveless fingers closed on his hand with sudden strength. 'He . . . he mustn't know.'

The kind man at her bedside did not press her with more questions. He seemed to sense her extreme distress. But his hand remained on hers, and though he was not Clyde, and Clyde was the only person she wanted with her despite her protest, Peter's presence provided its own kind of reassurance.

At length, driven by the need to talk to the one person who seemed to understand her and accept her without any demands, Sara unburdened herself voluntarily. Perhaps it was Peter's complete lack of censure, she thought, that made talking to him so easy, or perhaps it was just a gentleness and humaneness of manner. She held nothing back.

Now and then her eyes went to his face. Their expression was always the same; attentive, concerned. A good man, Sara thought, and understood anew why he was so respected in the company.

'Clyde should be told,' said Peter, when she was silent.

'No!' Sea-green eyes filled with sudden panic. 'He *is* the father.'

'I know.'

'And it's not his fault that you decided to call off the marriage.' The hand that held hers tightened. 'You're being unfair to him, Sara. He's man enough to make his own decisions. But he can't make them without knowing the facts.'

'No.' Blindly she shook her head. 'I know what he'd decide. He'd marry me.'

'Would that be so terrible? You love him.'

'I love him, yes. But after what happened he no longer loves me.' She pushed herself a little way up against the pillow. 'It wouldn't work, Peter. You must see that. He would resent me—resent us both.' She closed her eyes. 'I couldn't bear that.'

'Have you thought how hard it will be?' Peter asked.

'I'll have to manage.'

'Do you have any financial resources? From what you've told me. . . .'

Her eyes fluttered open. 'I'll be dancing. In a day or two I'll be back on stage.'

'No, my dear, you will not,' Peter said compassionately. 'The doctor made that quite clear.'

The small oval face took on a look of sheet-white transparency. The fingers resting in Peter's hand grew rigid. 'I'll manage,' Sara said. And then, more fiercely, 'I *will* manage, Peter, I promise you that.'

There was silence after her words. Long minutes of silence. Tired by the emotion expended in the discussion, as much as by the medication she had received, Sara closed her eyes once more. Peter did not speak. Only the warmth

of the hand that held hers revealed that he had
not left her side.

At length, breaking into her thoughts, she heard
him say, 'There *is* a solution.'

'You're suggesting I teach,' she said, putting into
words the trend of her own new thoughts.

'You're a brave girl. One of the bravest I
know.' There was admiration in his tone. 'No,
my dear, I wasn't thinking of teaching. Marry
me, Sara.'

Heavy lids jerked open to reveal the surprise in
the green eyes. 'You can't mean that!'

'Why so astonished, Sara?' There was a new
expression in his face, one she had never seen
before. 'It's not the first time I've proposed to
you.'

'I know. But circumstances have changed. . . .'

'You're carrying another man's child. And you
love him.' The tone was matter-of-fact.

She stared at him, bewildered. 'Yes.'

'Have you forgotten that *I* love *you*? What's
happened? The fact that you're human hasn't
changed that.'

Sara felt tears gather behind her lids. She tried
to blink them back, yet the eyes that met Peter's
were shimmering with emotion. 'I didn't know
there were men like you,' she whispered.

'I could give you a good life, Sara. My house
is just a few hours from Cape Town. When I'm
not working with the company we'd be together.'

'The baby. Clyde's baby. . . .'

'I'd love it as my own. And we'd have others,
Sara.'

'You're tempting me, Peter, you know that, don't you?' Looking at him, noting the strong chin beneath the firm mouth, the humour and the gentleness in the brown eyes, Sara knew that if she could never love another man as she had loved Clyde, if she had to settle for second best, she would find nobody better than Peter Burod.

His smile was surprisingly boyish for a man in his late forties. 'I want to tempt you.'

'Peter . . .' somehow she had to get through to him, 'I like you so very much. But I don't love you.' Her voice dropped to a whisper. 'I don't know if I ever will.'

'I love you. After Lisa died I didn't think I could ever feel strongly about a woman again.' He bent, and she felt his lips touch her forehead before going to her lips with surprising pressure. 'I won't press you for an answer today, Sara. Just think about it.'

When the sun was shining Kalk Bay must surely be one of the loveliest places on earth, Sara thought as she made her graceful high-stepped way along the sand. The sky was a powder blue above a vivid tabloid of forests and mountains and sea. A light breeze skimmed the water, ruffling the tops of the waves. In the fishing harbour the anchored boats rolled on the swell. A small boat had just put in with a catch of Cape snoek, and children were crowded in excitement around it, while above it, no less excited, a few hungry seagulls screamed. Kalk Bay had provided the setting for many a painting. On a day like this it was easy to see why.

Sara chose a spot near a clump of rocks. She spread her towel on the sand and took off her beach-gown. Before lying down she glanced at her figure. Still no obvious rounding. The only concession she had made to her pregnancy was the substitution of a one-piece bathing-suit for her bikini.

It was good to be out of doors again, with the smell of salt in her nostrils and the crash of the surf in her ears. Strange too, for until the day of her collapse every waking moment had been spent at rehearsals. Not only that, she could not remember when she had been here alone. The last time had been with Clyde. They had romped in the waves, and at sunset, when the fishermen and the holidaymakers had left the beach, Clyde had kissed her with a thoroughness that had made her dizzy with a desire she had not dreamed existed.

Thoughts of Clyde always brought pain. The struggle to forget him was far from over. It seemed there was nowhere she could go where there were no memories. But forget him she must.

She had come here to think. Not about Clyde—she knew he was lost to her—but about Peter. Kind, gentle Peter who understood and forgave everything and yet wanted her to be his wife.

'It wouldn't be fair to marry you feeling the way I do,' Sara had protested once.

'Let me the judge of what's fair,' he had smiled.

A little way distant two small children played with a beach-ball while a noisy terrier yapped at their heels. Sara watched the scene in amusement—and then suddenly she stiffened. On the periphery of her vision a man was walking. He was tall and well-built and his movements had a lithe ease. The breeze blew his fair hair backwards from his head. Clyde! Her hand went to her throat in panic as she stared at him.

'Stop it!' she told herself firmly. 'You can't forever see Clyde in every tall stranger. Get a grip on yourself or you'll make your life a total misery.'

Very deliberately she turned her eyes away from the man and back to the sea. The waves looked tempting. No undue exertion, the doctor had warned, no dancing. . . . At the same time he had said that walking and swimming would be good for her.

The water was warm, the waves gently rolling. Lifting her feet from the sandy sea-floor, Sara lay back and let the swell carry her. The rhythmic movement had a calming effect; she could feel the tension draining from her.

When a pair of strong hands gripped her shoulders she went rigid. For just a moment she kept her eyes closed. There was familiarity in the touch of the hands, in the feel of the long fingers against her bare skin.

She was dreaming, she told herself; she had to be. The grip tightened and she opened her eyes, slowly, unwillingly, and found herself staring into a taut chiselled face.

'Clyde. . . .' The name was wrenched from a parched throat.

'Little idiot!'

'You're angry. . . .'

'What the hell did you think you were doing? Trying to kill yourself?'

The blue eyes were like steel. Around his nostrils the skin was white. Sara looked at him uncomprehendingly, drinking in every line and crevice of the beloved face.

'I was swimming,' she said uncertainly.

'So far out of your depth?' Clipped. Precise.

The words made an impact on her. She tore her gaze from his face and looked shorewards. She was far from the beach, and she was not a strong swimmer. Lulled by the gentle motion of the waves, she had let the current carry her farther out than she had realised. A chill ran through her as she realised that she could indeed have been drowned.

She tried to struggle away from Clyde, to stand, and found herself being drawn closer against him, her feet touching his calves. She understood that if she touched bottom her head would be submerged.

'Let me go,' she whispered.

'In good time.' The anger had left his face and his voice had become a seductive drawl. 'So my little swan-maiden has turned into a mermaid.'

'I thought I saw you, on the beach. . . .'

'And that's why you tried to drown yourself?' An odd gleam in his eyes.

'Don't say that! Anyway, I decided it couldn't be you. And I wasn't trying to drown. . . .' The words caught in her throat as his hands slid slowly down her back to clasp her waist. The movement sent a torrent of desire cascading through her veins.

'D-do you have to do that?' she asked bumpily.

'You used to like it.' The hand lingered on her waist, curved forward around her stomach. 'You've gained weight.'

Only Clyde could be quite so perceptive. Careful, she thought, very careful.

'Perhaps the water makes me feel different,' she shrugged.

'Could be. Why aren't you at rehearsal?'

So he did not know! Incredibly, he did not know what had happened. And she did not intend telling him. 'We had the day off,' she managed unsteadily.

'And you're spending it alone?' He was so close to her that the salt-warmed breath fanned her cheek. Every inch of her was against him, the strong legs against her feet, the tautness of thighs hard against her own legs, the roughness of a hairy chest making sensuous contact with her bare skin where the costume did not cover her.

His voice was husky as he said, 'You feel just as sexy as ever.'

'Clyde. . . .'

'Sara,' he mocked raggedly. 'Keep still, poppet, you know you want me to kiss you.'

God, how she wanted him to kiss her! She wanted it with every nerve and fibre of her being.

His mouth was descending and she did not try to evade it. His hands were moulding themselves along her figure, welding her to him. She was up hard against the wall of his body, and there was a tightening of muscles which left her in no doubt that he wanted her as much as she wanted him.

His lips pushed hers apart easily. Her hands lifted to clasp his neck and buried themselves convulsively in his hair.

He was kissing her hungrily, and she was responding with a matching ardour. There was no thought, no past, no future. There was only the vastness of the African sky overhead, the tug and swell of the waves, the hardness of the long male body tight against hers.

She felt it quite suddenly—a tiny bubble-like movement in the region of her stomach, like the merest whisper of a butterfly's wing. Clyde could not have felt it, it was too slight a movement. Yet instinctively she pulled away.

'Sara. . . .' Again his voice was ragged. 'Sara darling. . . .'

'No, Clyde.'

'You want me.'

Yes, I want you. I want you as I've never wanted anything in my life. But our child just moved for the first time. *Our* child, Clyde!

'We could still get married. Darling, don't fight me.'

A wife and a baby. A burden to him. Belinda's words floating over the sea to her from that shrub-covered arbour.

'My career. Clyde, that hasn't changed,' she lied, every word piercing her in a raw stab of pain.

'Forget your career.' A hand went to her chin, forcing it upwards. For a long moment blue eyes searched green ones that were moist with tears.

'You want me,' he said, so softly that she saw the words rather than heard them over the waves.

'No!'

His face changed. The tautness was back. A muscle moved in the long line of the jaw and something flickered in his eyes. Deliberately he bent to her again. There was no time to twist away, even had she wanted to. His kiss was harder now, seductive, tantalising, yet lacking in tenderness. She understood that he was punishing her for hurting him. He did not know how much she was hurting herself.

She tried to close her mouth to him, but his strength was greater than hers. Besides, as her lips were forced apart an anguished hunger exploded inside her, so that she wanted only to be closer to him, part of him. . . .

The waves broke about them, but neither one of them noticed the movement of the surf. There was only the sensuousness of two wet bodies straining together, the fury of conflicting emotions contained in their embrace—joy and anger, hope and despair, exultation and a terrible grief for what would never be experienced again.

'Clyde,' Sara groaned helplessly when he lifted his head for breath. 'I don't . . . we can't. . . .'

'The hell we can't!' he said fiercely. 'Grow up, Sara. Don't you know what you want?'

She thought he would kiss her again, but instead he turned them both shorewards. He held her to him until they reached shallow water. Then he released her abruptly.

She turned to him as they came on to the sand. 'Clyde, I wish I could. . . .'

She stopped herself just in time. I wish I could explain, was what she had started to say. But she could *not* explain. Not today, probably never.

She took a step away from him and looked up. In the white swimsuit he was as superb a specimen of a man as she had ever seen. Broad shoulders tapered to a narrow waist, long legs were taut and muscled. There was not a spare ounce of flesh on the bronzed body. His fair hair was plastered wetly back from his head, and his eyes were as blue as the sky above.

Dominating all else was an impression of maleness, of virility, of a compelling sexual appeal which left Sara feeling weak despite her determination to be strong.

She opened her mouth, not knowing quite what she meant to say, when the breath caught in her throat. A girl had come up to them. Sara had not seen her approach. She was tall and beautiful with all her curves in the right places, and as fair as Clyde himself. She threw Sara a glance that was sharp with dislike, then looked up at Clyde with a pouting smile.

'Darling, I wondered where you'd got to.'

'I went for a swim.'

'You might have waited for me, darling.' A hand slid possessively around his waist as she looked at Sara with an expression that said 'Private property, keep away.'

Clyde looked faintly irritated, and Sara noticed that he made no attempt to dislodge the hand. 'You were talking to your friends,' was all he said.

'Oh yes, and darling, they were all so happy that we're together again. Do you know, Ted asked me out, but I told him no, that it's just a matter of time now before we. . . .'

'Andrea,' Clyde interrupted, 'I want you to meet Sara Demaine. Sara, this is Andrea Stanford.'

'The dancer.' Perfectly painted lips thinned. 'How nice. Clyde darling, we really must be going.'

Sara forced a smile. Somehow she kept it plastered to her face while the baby—her baby and Clyde's—moved inside her once more. 'I must be getting along too,' she said with all the composure she could muster.

She felt drained and numb as she watched them walk away. Clyde and Andrea Stanford, the girl whose father could do so much to help pave Clyde's way to a glittering future. 'Don't cry,' she told herself fiercely, as she felt the tears welling in her eyes. 'It's all over. Just get off this beach without crying.'

Sara accepted Peter's third proposal. In deference to her health the wedding was quiet. Madame Olga was there, and all Sara's friends from the company. Family was represented only by Aunt Mary, who journeyed from Durban to take the place of the parents who had died long ago. And there was Lynn, unconnected with dancing, and the owner of an antique shop in the village that was not far from Peter's wine estate Morning Glow. Lynn had been Sara's closest friend at school. It was a friendship which time and distance had never dulled.

'Do you, Peter, take this woman. . . .'

The words 'I will' were spoken in a tone that was low and firm. If the memory of Peter's first wife stood in the shadows there was nothing in his manner to indicate it.

'Do you, Sara, take this man. . . .'

'I will.' Faintly. And then more firmly, 'I will'. And all the while a part of her, outside of her so it seemed, was weeping. Clyde, you should be standing beside me today, not this very kind man who has just promised to cherish me till death us do part.

And then Peter was kissing her, and they were being showered with confetti, and there was laughter and talk and a buzz of congratulations. Sara smiled with the rest. A not-too-perceptive stranger would have said she was a happy bride; the desolation which filled her was hidden deep inside. Turning a laughing face to Peter, she understood that although he knew her love for Clyde still existed, she must not let him know the extent of it. She owed Peter that much at least.

The honeymoon was spent at Morning Glow. Morning Glow was a name with which Sara had long been familiar. The wine estate on the Garden Route was famed for its loveliness. Generations of Burods had lived here. Peter, the present owner, drove out from Cape Town whenever he could. The demands made on the choreographer were great. At Morning Glow he could relax. Somehow he had managed to take ten days from his busy routine to be alone with his new bride. They were happy days. The sensitivity which Peter had displayed from the beginning was with him still as he made his bride his wife. There was a gentleness in his love-making, a passion that was both sweet yet undemanding. Sara tried to respond to him as best she could. There was an ease and affection between them which made her think at times that she succeeded. Then she would remember the wildness of her ardour when she had lain in Clyde's arms, and she knew that much of her response was largely forced. If Peter was aware of sham, and disappointed by it, he did not say so; he seemed content with the measure of love that Sara could give him.

And there *was* love between them. A very different sort of love from the overwhelming, all-consuming emotion she had experienced once, yet love nevertheless. Living with Peter, listening quietly while he spoke of his hopes and dreams, she knew that the man she had thought of as kind and thoughtful and sensitive was in fact all the things she had imagined—and more, and little by little her affection for him increased.

The honeymoon over, Peter had reluctantly to leave her and drive back to Cape Town. Sara asked to be taken along, but he was adamant that she should stay at Morning Glow. She had the baby to think of, he told her. His concern could not have been greater if he had been the father of the coming child. Clyde's part in the fathering was never discussed. When Peter spoke of the approaching birth, it was with quiet joy. There was no doubt in Sara's mind that he would look upon the child as his own.

She was lucky, she knew. On her own, she could have provided her baby with much love but only the essentials in comfort. With Peter Burod as its father, the child would have every luxury. She hoped he would never regret ·having made ·another's man's child his own.

Looking over the purple vineyards, Sara often had to convince herself that she was really the mistress of this glorious estate; that she had a wealthy and adoring husband who wanted only to spoil her. She knew she should be totally happy.

She *would* be totally happy—if only she could shut Clyde from her mind. But how to shut him out, when the life that he had placed inside her was growing every day? When the memories of a love that had meant more to her even than her dancing still provoked pain?

For Peter's sake and her own, she had to forget Clyde. When she was awake, she could apply the self-discipline that was so much a part of her ballerina's make-up, and force herself to think of other things. But at night, when her unconscious took over, her dreams were of a tall lean man, with thick fair hair and eyes that were deeply intelligent. And in the mornings, with the dreams still very vivid, she would wake up feeling drained. She *would* forget, she told herself despairingly. She *had* to.

On a morning in early summer she sat on the verandah, staring out towards the sea. The house was built high into a cliff overlooking the vineyards from one angle, the sea from another. It had been aptly named Morning Glow, Sara thought. It was not long since the sun had risen, and sea and land were bathed in a translucent radiance. Everywhere was in an intense clarity, a crispness that seemed to infuse the very air itself, giving it a champagne-like quality which Sara had never experienced in the city.

At the soft sound of feet on the grass, she turned. The housekeeper had come to take her tray. Her name was Lettie; she had soft generous features and a friendly smile, and Sara had taken to her from the start. The liking was evidently reciprocated, for Lettie went out of her way to do small things that would please her. She smiled at Sara as she held out a newspaper.

'Thank you, Lettie,' Sara smiled back, marvelling not for the first time at the speed with which the staff had accepted her.

As Lettie made her way back to the house, Sara took up the newspaper and began to turn the pages. First the entertainment section, where she devoured the latest reviews. Any mention of ballet left her feeling stimulated yet wistful. It had been hard to accept that she had to stop dancing, that the part she had looked forward to for so long now belonged to Maria, her understudy. She wondered when she would dance again. After the baby was born there would be a period that was only for mothering. But one day. . . .

She had never read the newspaper as thoroughly as she did now. There had never been time to do more than skim the headlines. Now the papers were her link with the city and a life in which she had once been very involved.

The photograph on the society page sent her suddenly rigid. Clyde was staring up at her—Clyde, with his arm around a curvaceous blonde whom she recognised. For a long moment Sara gazed fixedly at the photo, unable to move her eyes to the words below. It was as if Clyde was holding her gaze, defying her to look away. Clyde, unfamiliar in dress suit, his head just slightly inclined towards the girl at his side, his appearance more distinguished than ever.

A great trembling took Sara as the blur of print began to clear. The premonition of disaster made no sense—no reason why Clyde should not be photographed with Andrea Stanford. Yet as she began to read she knew without seeing the words what they would tell her.

The engagement was announced of Dr Clyde Montgomery to Andrea Stanford. Andrea's father was well known in the world of medicine, and the wedding was to take place shortly.

The pages fluttered from nerveless fingers. The blood drained from Sara's face, and her limbs were like water. Inside her she felt a small flutter. The baby had kicked. It was a movement Sara felt seldom; sometimes she wondered whether the baby was as strong as it should be, whether it had been affected by her collapse some months earlier. That it should choose to move now seemed symbolic, a token of protest against the decision its father had chosen to make.

What had she expected? she asked herself unhappily. That Clyde remain faithful to her memory? That he pursue the path towards his career ambitions alone? He had not asked her to break their engagement. And from Andrea Sara had gathered that this new engagement was just a matter of time.

If bitterness was unreasonable, it burned within her notwithstanding. Both sets of parents were delighted, the announcement said. And why not? Andrea was acquiring a husband who would stir the senses of any woman. Sara remembered the conversation she had overheard. Andrea had taken up with someone else, Belinda had said. Evidently Andrea had returned to her first love. Knowing Clyde, having experienced the impact of his sensual maleness, that was something Sara could understand.

As for Clyde, in marrying Dr Stanford's daughter he had set himself firmly on the path to success. No wonder the respective parents were glad.

What of Clyde's feelings? Had he forgotten the

dancer he had sworn to love to the end of his days?
Or had he managed to convince himself that what
he had felt for Sara had never been more than infatuation for a girl who came from a world so different from his own? Did he love Andrea? Perhaps
he did, for she was beautiful. Even if he did not,
perhaps he had not ignored the benefits her position could bring him. There was the memory of
the windy day in the Clifton apartment. 'I mean to
be rich and famous,' he had said. There had been
conviction in his tone. Now, through Andrea
Stanford, he was assured that his ambition would
be fulfilled.

Suddenly Sara was on her feet. The joy had gone
out of the day. She did not see the gracious house,
the loveliness of the vineyards and the sea. There
was only pain, a searing pain that was even worse
than that which she had experienced on overhear-
ing the conversation which had led her to sever the
relationship with the man she loved. Stumbling a
little, she made her way inside. She wanted only to
be in her room, alone, free to weep until her eyes
were drained of tears.

Another morning, a week or two later, Sara was
again sitting on the verandah, but today the sky
was overcast, the sea a sullen wind-chopped grey.
Restlessly she shifted in her chair, trying to ease
her swollen body into a more comfortable position.

She had made it a habit to take a daily walk.
Accustomed as she was to the sea, the wild beauty
of this particular coastline never failed to enchant
her. With Bruno, Peter's big labrador, racing in

front of her, she would walk along the beach, the dainty high-instepped dancer's feet moulding themselves to the soft sand, the fine golden grains sifting between her toes. The morning walks had become as much a part of her life as the practice at the barre had once been.

Today, however, the effort to negotiate the path down to the beach seemed an insuperable ordeal. Watching a fishing-boat tossed this way and that on the angry waves, she wondered if the weather had affected her mood. She was filled with an intense unease, coupled with an odd inertia—an inertia which the baby inside her seemed to share. Never active, today she could not remember feeling it move at all.

'No walk today, Miss Sara?'

Sara looked up at Lettie, who had appeared silently at her side bearing a tray with yogurt and orange juice. The housekeeper's face was thoughtful. Over the months her concern for Sara had never wavered, a fact Sara appreciated, for with Peter away all week—even now he was in Cape Town, hard at work on the choreography for a new ballet—she was often lonely.

'The weather. . . .' She tried to smile.

Lettie forbore making the comment that Sara had walked in worse weather. Putting down the tray on a small side table, she asked, 'When is the next appointment with the doctor?'

'Friday.'

'Perhaps you should go today.'

'Oh no, I'll wait.'

Lettie was at the door leading into the house when an anguished gasp brought her spinning around. Sara's face was white, with bands of sweat on the high forehead. The big sloe eyes were panic-stricken and the slender body was twisted in pain.

Within moments she had relaxed somewhat, though her face had not regained its colour. 'I'm sorry, Lettie.' The words came uncertainly through white lips. 'I don't know what . . . what came over me.'

'The baby?'

'No.' With a conviction she was far from feeling, 'Nothing to do with the baby. . . .'

'Come to bed, Miss Sara. Then I will phone the doctor.'

'Stop fussing, Lettie,' Sara said weakly. 'I'll be fine, really I. . . .'

Her words trailed away in another gasp of pain. Instinctively she seized Lettie's hand, gripping it fiercely, only relaxing its hold when the spasm had passed.

'The baby,' Lettie said again.

'It can't be! It's not due yet. Gastric 'flu probably.'

'I will phone the doctor.' Lettie wasted no more words arguing. 'Then Mr Peter in Cape Town. He must come. George will drive you to the hospital.'

There was no withstanding the usually smiling housekeeper once her mind was made up. By the time she had been ensconced in the car, George the gardener at the wheel, Sara was no longer even in the mood to protest. The spasms were coming frequently, at regular intervals, and the pain was severe.

'Mr Peter is coming,' Lettie said, as she covered the trembling girl with a rug. 'He is leaving Cape Town now.'

'Yes. . . .' through nerveless lips. But in her mind an anguished cry. Clyde. . . . Clyde, you should be with me. The baby is coming. *Our* baby. Oh, Clyde, I need you!

Sara was never to remember much of the next hours. Vaguely she was aware of people, bustling around her. Dr Simons, kind, competent, calming her with his own lack of panic. A nurse wheeling her to the labour ward, then to the operating theatre. The moment when the baby was born, and the odd hush that followed. A glimpse of the doctor's face, more tight-lipped than she had seen him. And then an injection. Oblivion. . . .

Someone was sitting beside her as she woke. Peter. . . . And that was odd, because it should have been Clyde. Clyde's baby.

And then her mind began to clear. This was Peter by her side—her husband. He was smiling down at her, and in his eyes was a look of incredible sadness.

Memory returned—the pains, the hurried drive to the hospital, the birth and the doctor's expression in the moment before she had been anaesthetised.

'What did we have?' And when Peter did not answer, 'The baby? A boy or a girl?'

The look in her husband's face deepened. 'Sara. . . . Sara, my very dearest, it was a girl. But . . .' she heard the break in his voice, 'she. . . .'

'Died?' Sara felt the frenzied sob at the back of her throat.

'She's alive, but only just. She's not expected to live.'

There were no words in her as she stared at her husband. She did not know that to Peter she seemed only eyes, enormous sloe-shaped eyes from which all colour seemed to have vanished. Eyes that were moist and brilliant with distress. The eyes of Odette, the swan-maiden, adrift in a world where meaning, as she knew it, had fled.

'No!' she gasped at length, blindly.

The hand holding hers grew firmer, as if Peter tried to infuse her with his love and strength. 'Sara dearest, whatever happens it will be for the best. Cruel as that may sound. The baby ... she's so very ill.'

'No,' she said again, and moved her eyes away from his.

He could not know the meaning her 'no' entailed. That it was confirmation that what had been between her and Clyde should never have been. The love that had flamed between them like some lovely vital fire. The baby that had been produced as a result. Clyde, she cried, over and over again. During the pregnancy there had been the hope that their child would be the one tangible product of a love she might never know again, a constant memory, alive and wonderful. Now even that was to be denied her.

Tears welled in Sara's eyes, she let them fall unchecked. As a mother she wept for the baby she would never know. As a woman she wept for a love of which there was nothing left.

Peter sat by her side, silently. Almost as if he knew the thoughts that passed through her mind, she would think later. It was a measure of his empathy that he was able to understand; that he could

accept without intruding, even though that acceptance must cause him pain of a different kind.

Peter was still with her when the doctor came.
The latter was matter-of-fact, but with it he was
kind. There were things Sara had to know, knowledge which she could not be spared. He tried to
soften the telling as much as he could.

She had a rare disease, he told her, one that had
been dormant inside her for many years, but which
the pregnancy had brought to the fore. It was this
which had brought about her collapse on stage on
that night. She could lead a normal life, he said.
But he did not know if she could have more babies.
And she had to avoid undue physical exertion.

It took a few seconds for his meaning to make its
impact. When it did, she stared at him wide-eyed.
'No more dancing?'

Something came and went in an expression that
was outwardly calm. 'No more dancing.'

Was it possible for all one's world to be shattered
in the space of a few short hours? Sara's eyes went
from the doctor to Peter. There was compassion in
both faces.

Still in the grip of shock—surely all this was
some nightmare from which she would wake?—
Sara passed a tongue over dry lips. 'I can't give up
dancing.' And then, with sudden vehemence, 'I
won't!'

'You have no choice, my dear.' The doctor's
voice was very quiet.

'Sara, your health is more important than anything else.' Peter was bending over her, his voice
was urgent. 'Don't you understand that?'

She pulled her hands from his and put them over

her face. Her heart was beating very fast, and at
the back of her throat was a lump so big that she
could hardly swallow.

'Darling. . . .'

'Leave me,' she managed, without lifting her fingers from her eyes. 'Just . . . just let me be alone.'

CHAPTER FOUR

TIME passed, and Sara grew stronger. Soon she was walking along the beach again every day. Bruno the labrador was still her constant companion. But now the dog did not always run ahead. Often he stayed at her side, his head nuzzling her legs, his tongue going out to lick her fingers. It was as if he sensed her unhappiness and wanted to comfort her.

Now and then Sara reached out and stroked the shaggy head. Bruno was more comforting than he knew. But he could not erase the sense of numbness, could not fill the emptiness that was like a vacuum inside her. Just as Peter was unable to do.

And Peter had tried. He had put as much of himself into trying as it was possible for a man to do. Sara, grateful to him, had tried, on her part, to respond. Nevertheless, she knew her husband was not fooled by her façade of outward cheerfulness; his expression told her that.

The baby had lived two days. Its death had been merciful, the doctor had said. Sara, trying to shake off the mantle of depression, had tried to believe him.

Peter had brought her home from the hospital. He himself had taken leave of absence from the ballet company. Sara had attempted to dissuade him, knowing the importance of his work, but he had been unexpectedly firm. No man was indispensable, he had said. Another choreographer could perfect the groundwork he had laid for a new ballet. When she was better they would return to Cape Town together.

'You're so good to me.' Sara had trailed a finger along the familiar lines of his face.

'I love you,' he had said simply.

She loved him too, as much as it was possible to love another human being without being actually in love with him. There had been a time when she would have considered her feelings for Peter as being the ultimate in love. Had she never met Clyde, Sara knew, her love for Peter would have been a deep and completely satisfying emotion. There would have been no sense of incompleteness, of knowing that love was more than sharing and gentleness and compassion. But she had met Clyde, and there was no way of rationalising away the fact that there was a part of her, a deeply passionate part of her, which would never be fulfilled by her husband.

The knowledge induced a feeling of guilt. Clyde was in the past. He had no right to intrude in the night when Peter held her in his arms. She had no right to think of him. . . .

Clyde was never mentioned between them. And yet his ghost was always there, an invisible barrier between them. It drove Sara to be extra attentive to her husband. When they made love, it led her to respond with an ardour she did not feel. Peter was the best thing that ever happened to her. She would not hold herself back from him, in any way whatsoever.

A month went by. There were phone-calls from

the company. It was time for Peter to go back. He
assumed that Sara would return with him, and
when she said she would remain behind at Morning
Glow, he was at first puzzled, then upset.

'Dr Simons said you could go.'

'I'm not ready,' she protested.

'You need to get away from here. Your place is
in Cape Town. With the people you know.'

'Not yet,' Sara insisted.

'It won't be easy to be with dancers. I know
that. . . .'

'Just a little more time,' she begged.

Peter's lips softened. He was never immune to
her pleading. 'A month,' he said. 'I'll visit you every
weekend.'

Two months passed. As Sara walked along the
beach with Bruno she knew that she could no
longer postpone the return to Cape Town. Today
was Friday. Peter would be coming for the weekend. Yesterday his tone on the phone had signified
a growing impatience. When he left Morning Glow
on Monday he expected Sara to go with him.

By late afternoon he had not arrived. Something
must have cropped up, she thought, some unexpected difficulty in a ballet which needed cor-
recting.

The shadows lengthened on the ground.
Afternoon became evening. Sara was growing
worried. Then the sound of the telephone rent the
stillness of the empty house; there had been an
accident, and Peter had been badly hurt. He was
unconscious.

Lettie, hearing a scream, ran into the living-
room. She was just in time to catch Sara's slender

form as it slumped into a faint.

'Say you'll do it, Sara.'

'I'll think about it, Lynn.'

'I have to know today.' Lynn's mop of red curls was like a ball of flame in the sunlight. Eyes that were normally laughing were now serious. 'I have to book right away if I'm to take Mom on the cruise.'

Sara looked at her friend, then away. Lynn's request had been unexpected. She wanted Sara to take over the running of her antique shop in the village while she took her mother, who had been ill and was now recuperating, on an ocean cruise.

'Well, Sara?'

'I don't know. It would mean. . . .' She stopped.

'It would mean leaving Morning Glow each day,' Lynn said crisply. 'Best thing that could happen to you.'

'You make it sound like a prison,' Sara protested.

'In a way it is.' Lynn put out an impulsive hand. 'Don't get me wrong. It's a lovely house. But you're letting yourself become a hermit. A period of mourning is normal, but you've been living like a recluse for more than a year. Since Peter died. . . . You should have gone back to Cape Town long ago.'

'I can't go back to dancing,' Sara said unsteadily. 'You know that.'

'And you've no desire to do anything else.' A rueful grin. 'I know that too. But there are other interests out there in the world. You could find a new niche in one of them.'

'And you think running an antique shop is where I'll find it?'

'I didn't say that.' A vigorous shake of the red curls. 'Though I know you'd do it well. You've a natural taste for lovely things, old things. . . .' She paused. 'I need a favour, Sara. By running the shop you help me and yourself at the same time.'

'In the light of such eloquent pleading how can I refuse?' For the first time Sara grinned, a gamin-like expression curving the soft upward-tilted lips.

The first step, thought Lynn who was watching her, and heard Sara ask, 'When do I start?'

Tuesday, said Lynn, and began to talk about the shop. She would be away a few months. There was much Sara would need to know.

'How do I get hold of you?'

'You won't be able to,' Lynn laughed. 'You'll have to cope as best you can.'

'Why do I get the feeling that I've been manoeuvred into something?' But Sara's protest was a smiling one. 'All right, Lynn. You've been the best friend anyone could want. I'll start on Tuesday.'

Sara was humming as she polished the collec-tion of copper pots. She had been at the Antique Den three weeks and was enjoying the experience more than she would have thought possible. Though she loved beautiful things, her knowledge of antiques had till now been limited. Since her thrust into the situation, she had spent much time reading the books Lynn had left with her. The more she understood and recognised, the more fascinated she became with the objects by which she was surrounded.

There had been one postcard from Lynn. No questions about the shop—almost as if she wanted no comebacks, Sara thought. Instead, in Lynn's breezy style, there had been the news that her mother, desperately in need of a convalescing holiday, was responding well to the trip. The change had affected her whole mental outlook.

As her own outlook had been changed, Sara had thought, putting down the card. Not till she had been faced with the necessity of travelling into the village every morning had she understood how limited her life had become. The contact with customers was unexpectedly stimulating, the responsibility of having to run the shop on her own a challenge. Much as she missed dancing—she would always miss it, she knew—she was learning that other careers existed, and that they could be satisfying. For the first time she began to wonder what avenues she herself could pursue after Lynn returned.

From a financial point of view she had no need to work, for Peter had left her well provided for. And yet work she must. Mentally she blessed Lynn's persuasiveness. Now, when she returned to Morning Glow in the evenings she was able to see the estate for what it was: a place of exceptional beauty, yet a prison of her own making unless she reached out.

Perhaps Lynn would let her come in with her as a partner. It was just possible that an input of capital was what she needed. If not that, perhaps she could start a gallery. This stretch of coast was a haven both for artists and retired people with money. That combination might make a gallery viable.

'. . . . where is the collection of Cape silver?'

The words did not penetrate her consciousness as much as the voice. A low voice, vibrant and vital. A voice that appeared in her dreams.

She was turned a little away from him. He would not be able to see her face, just as she could not see his. But she could feel the sparks between them and tried to tell herself she was imagining things.

Her whole body had grown rigid. She could feel tension extending from the base of her neck down her spine to toes which were normally a miracle of flexibility, could feel it in her chest, so that breathing was difficult.

'The collection of Cape silver,' he said again. There was a new inflection in his tone, as if he wondered why she did not answer him. Perhaps, too, the beginnings of recognition.

Through the tightness Sara managed, somehow, to take a breath. She did a half turn. 'In the far corner. . . .'

And then, turning fully, she lifted her head.

'Sara!'

'Hello, Clyde.' Her voice wobbled.

'My God, Sara!' He took a step towards her. His eyes were wide, and something worked in his throat. He was as surprised to see her as she was to see him, and as shocked. Any thought that he might have made a deliberate excuse to seek her out vanished. His shock was genuine.

Wordlessly she stared at him, drinking in the eyes that were more blue than she had remembered them, the nose that was strong and straight, the shock of fair hair that fell across the high forehead in a manner that was familiar, the firm line of the jaw above the proud thrust of throat. She was dreaming, she told herself wildly. It *must* be a dream, one from which she had no desire to waken.

'My God, Sara,' he said again, 'what are you doing here?'

'I——work here.'

'I don't believe it!' As the initial shock faded, she saw his eyes narrow, and she knew that she was not dreaming. This was happening, really happening, and what would follow might not be pleasant.

'You may as well believe it.' Her voice was light.

'Keeping shop?'

'As you see.'

His hands reached for hers without warning, clamping themselves around fragile wrists. The polishing cloth dropped from unsteady fingers as a tingling shot up her arms.

'Let me go!' It was hard to speak as if she meant it, when what she really wanted was to be close to him, to be kissed by him.

As if he had not heard her, the pressure increased. 'You're in between ballets, I suppose.'

Sara closed her eyes, just for a moment. There was just so much pain, surely, that a person could be expected to endure.

'I'm running this shop.'

He was so close to her that she could feel the vibrations of his body, could smell the warm clean male smell of him that was so uniquely his own. Go quickly, she pleaded silently, before I make a fool of myself in some way.

'Why?' he questioned harshly.

So he still did not know all that had happened.
In a way she was glad. There were many things she
wanted from Clyde Montgomery, even now, but
pity was not one of them.

She shrugged. 'Why not?'

'That's not an answer.'

His eyes were hard, speculative, contemptuous.
Without volition her own eyes shifted.

'Why?' he asked again. One hand went to her
chin, forcing it up, so that she had no choice but
to meet his gaze. 'Look at me when you talk.'

He had no right to behave like this, with arro-
gance and contempt. Their ways had parted. His
right to demand answers no longer existed.

'The pay is good,' she said, saying the first thing
that came to mind.

'And that's important to you? What about your
dancing?'

'It's easier than dancing,' she said, and hoped he
did not hear the bumpiness in her tone.

She heard the hiss of his breath. When he spoke
his voice was like ice. 'Somehow I never imagined
you as avaricious and lazy.'

Through her pain, she managed to match his
tone. 'Just as I,' she said, 'didn't take you for tact-
less. You were asking about Cape silver when you
came in. . . .'

'Are you going to show it to me?' His tone was
flat.

'What we have is in that part of the shop. . . .'

She gestured. 'When you know what you want
tell me and I'll let you know the price.'

'I've always known what I want.' An outrageous drawl. 'I'm just beginning to understand that it could have been had for the right price.'

His meaning was clear. Despite her striving for composure Sara felt herself pale. Clyde's hand was still on her chin. She was jerking away from him when he withdrew his hand of his own accord—as if the touch had been distasteful to him.

'I'm busy, Clyde.' She stared blindly past him. 'I've things to do. If you'd like to look around. . . .'

'Thank you, but no,' he said very quietly.

Without another word, not even a goodbye, he walked out of the shop.

It took all of Sara's self-discipline to negotiate the twenty-odd miles back to Morning Glow. Even now, hours later, she was as shaken by the encounter with Clyde as if it had just taken place. The foot that pressed down on the accelerator was like water, and when she looked at the hands that held the wheel she saw they were white-knuckled and taut.

'Something wrong, Miss Sara?' Lettie's face was concerned when her mistress came through the front door.

'Nothing, Lettie.' Sara tried to smile. 'I'm just tired. It's been a long day.'

'I'll bring you up some tea.' Lettie had taken over a nurturing role from the beginning, and had never abandoned it.

'Thank you,' Sara said gratefully. She began to walk towards the stairs, then turned back. 'Oh, and Lettie, I'm going to have a sleep. If anyone should call for me, I'm not available.'

An unnecessary remark, she realised as she made her way to the bedroom. Clyde would neither phone her nor make any attempt to see her. He did not know her new name nor where she lived. Even if he did, there was no reason why he should want to see her again.

Andrea. . . . The memory of the willowy blonde brought her up short. Clyde's wife would not tolerate her husband having anything to do with the girl to whom he had once been engaged. All things considered, her instructions to Lettie had been unnecessary.

Her head was throbbing as she lay down on the double bed she had once shared with Peter. Closing her eyes, she wondered if the meeting with Clyde would have been any different if she had been prepared for it. No, she decided, her responses would have been the same. Implacable Clyde might be, arrogant and openly contemptuous of Sara's style of life as he saw it, but nothing had robbed him of the dynamism that made him still the most attractive man she had ever met. Had she been forewarned of his coming, she would have been no less shaken.

There was relief in the thought that tomorrow was Sunday and that the shop would be closed. Though it was unlikely that Clyde would be back to look at the silver, Sara was glad of the respite the weekend would give her. Lynn had accused her of making Morning Glow a retreat; at this moment the emotional safety and privacy the house offered had never seemed more inviting.

When she awoke the next morning the sun was

already slanting through the blue sun-filter curtains. For a few moments she lay quite still, savouring the sound of the surf, and letting yesterday's memories wash over her. A night's sleep had gone a long way to restoring her sense of balance. She felt brimful of energy as she swung her feet over the side of the bed and made for the window.

It was a glorious day. The sea was very blue. The tide was coming in, and on the distant horizon a ship was making its way towards the port of Cape Town. The stretch of beach beneath Morning Glow was a dazzling strip of gold. It was ages since she had been on the sands. Since she had started work at the Antique Den not only her working days but also her spare time had been fully occupied. A day out of doors was the very break that she needed.

Lettie had prepared a breakfast of orange juice, croissants and a lightly poached egg, with a bunch of purple grapes to finish the meal.

'I can't manage this much!' Sara protested laughingly.

'You can, Miss Sara. You were always as skinny as a sparrow, but these last weeks. . . .' A disapproving shake of the head. 'What Mr Peter would think if he could see you!'

Mention of Peter brought a resurgence of sorrow. His death had touched Sara very deeply, and there was not a day that she did not think of him. But she had hardly thought of him yesterday, after Clyde had re-entered her life. The knowledge brought a sharp pang of guilt. If Peter had never managed to stir her senses as Clyde did so easily, she knew nevertheless that she would never again meet anyone quite so selfless and kind. The fact that her blood had raced at sight of Clyde, that she had longed to be in his arms, seemed to suggest disloyalty to a man who had been so good.

A little soberly she began to eat. The juice had been freshly squeezed and the grapes were tartly delicious. The rest of the meal was pushed aside.

'I can't manage any more,' she told the disapproving housekeeper, as she got to her feet. 'I'm going to spend the day on the beach.'

In her bedroom she changed into a bikini. About to slip a towelling gown over her shoulders, she was caught by her reflection in the mirror, and all at once her heart was beating uncomfortably fast.

The lilac bikini had been Clyde's favourite, but it was not the only one she possessed. What had prompted her to wear it today? Surely not the off-chance that he might see her, that in bringing back memories of moments that had been delightfully tender his new contemptuous mood might soften?

No! She shook herself impatiently. She was becoming fanciful if she imagined that her subconscious mind was influencing her actions. The chances of meeting Clyde were less than minimal. She meant to stay on the strip of sand which bordered Morning Glow. Though not officially private, that was in fact what the beach was. The holiday beach lay close to the village, half an hour's drive from here. If Clyde meant to spend the day at the sea, that was where he would be.

Besides, Clyde would be with Andrea. The last thing he would want was that his wife and his ex-fiancée should meet and spoil the day. For it would be spoiled. The one short meeting with Andrea had revealed a beautiful girl with a possessive manner.

There would be no relaxing if the three of them were thrown together.

Yet there was no reason to change into another bikini. Once she had made a great sacrifice for Clyde's sake. She knew it, though he never would. Now she owed him nothing. If she allowed a past memory to dictate her behaviour, she would be showing weakness. The first weakness would be a stepping-stone to the next. She would keep on the bikini she had originally chosen.

A little curious she studied herself in the mirror. It was a long while since she had looked at herself critically. The quiet months at Morning Glow had brought an apricot tan to her cheeks; against it her eyes were very green, her hair glossy. Her appearance had always been fragile, and that had not changed. The fragility extended to her body. A stranger looking at her might not have guessed that the slender body had once withstood the rigours demanded of a ballet dancer.

What she had not noticed before, Sara realised, was the sensuousness the bikini revealed. Small breasts were high and perfectly defined beneath the clinging fabric. If the waist was almost too tiny, it flared to hips that were softly rounded. The long thighs were smooth and shapely. Against the air of fragility, the overall curvaceousness had a hint of incongruity.

A slight breeze had risen as Sara came down to the beach. She took off her wrap and her sandals and left them by a pile of rocks. A long lazy day stretched ahead of her, and later she would read, but first she wanted to walk. Her body craved exercise. If dancing was denied her, walking was her only recourse.

Her spirits rose as she followed the water line. The breeze lifted her hair and blew it backwards, and the taste of salt was on her lips. The foam of the incoming waves eddied about her feet, curling about her ankles. She looked back once and saw the prints her feet had made, the only prints on a beach washed clear by the last tide. Here and there shells were sharp beneath her toes, and once she stopped to pick up a particularly lovely one.

Ahead of her the beach stretched golden and untrodden. The sound of the waves crashing on the rocks was a ceaseless roar. Sara had always loved the sea, never more than on a day like this one, when she was quite alone.

'Let the wind blow the cobwebs from your brain,' had been one of her grandmother's favourite sayings. Now, surrounded by sand and wind and sea, she knew the cobwebs that had clouded her thinking yesterday were gone.

The meeting with Clyde had been a shock. There had been too much between them for her to have reacted otherwise. His attitude had been wounding. Natural enough, she realised now, for he had never understood her rejection of him. And yet, as much as the meeting had unnerved her, there was no reason to let it dwell on her mind. It had been a chance encounter, one of those freak events that happen when one least expects them. It would not happen again.

So distraught had she been last night that it had not occurred to her to wonder what Clyde was doing in a small seaside village so far from his home. Even this morning, as she had dithered over

the choice of bikinis, there had been the worry that
she might run into him again.

Now she could think rationally, and she realised
that the possibility of another meeting was
unlikely. What had led Clyde to the Antique Den
in search of Cape silver was something she did not
know. Perhaps he had heard of the shop and made
a note to visit it if ever he was passing through the
village.

But passing through was all he could have been
doing. Perhaps he had been on his way back to
Cape Town from a medical convention. Unless he
had come here on a holiday.... A moment of
panic at the thought, for it would entail the possibility of another meeting. Then came the realisation
that he was not on holiday. If he had been, Andrea
would have been with him, and Sara doubted that
Clyde's wife would enjoy the very basic pleasures
which were all the village could provide.

Sara walked further and further. Now and then
the beach narrowed, so that there was no more
than a foot of sand between the rocks and the
jungle-like vegetation of the interior. Sometimes
there was no sand at all so that she had to climb,
nimble-footed, over great piles of black stone. And
then she would come to a new beach as private
and as unmarked by human feet as the one before.

She did not know how long she had been walking
when she saw the long shadow take form on the
sand beside her own. In the manner of shadows, it
was elongated to the point of exaggeration.
Nevertheless, compared to her own, it suggested
that its owner was a tall person indeed.

Sara stifled the cry of alarm that rose to her lips.

She was in a small cove now. Any stranger might have come down from the underbrush to walk beside the water, just as she was doing. In a moment the shadow would move beyond hers as the person went past her. There was no cause for panic.

She went on walking, trying to keep her rhythm steady. Only when it was clear that the person at her back did not mean to pass her, did she turn. Her eyes, controlled to hide her fright, slanted up upward to Clyde's face.

CHAPTER FIVE

'You followed me.' Her accusation was cool.

'Good morning, and how are you?' he asked mockingly. 'Thank you, I'm very well.'

Despite herself she flushed. 'After the way you spoke to me yesterday no civilities are necessary.'

'Unnecessary perhaps, but polite all the same.'

Since when had there been need for politeness between them? Loving, in all its forms, had pervaded the whole of their relationship. All the niceties had, quite naturally, been taken care of.

'Why did you follow me?' Sara demanded.

'I wanted to talk to you.'

Strange how her heart was racing. No matter that the love that had once existed between them had vanished, at least as far as Clyde was concerned, it seemed she could no more prevent herself responding to him than she could stop breathing.

'We've nothing to talk about.' Her voice was very low.

'Oh yes, Sara, I think we have.' His tone was hard.

She was frightened all at once. There were things she had resolved she would never tell Clyde. She would not let herself weaken on that point. But standing up to him might not be easy. The break in their relationship had revealed a new aspect of his personality. Clyde could be inflexible.

She bit her lip, then deliberately let it go. Any

hint of uncertainty would be pounced on as a sign of weakness. If she meant to stand up to him, the sooner she did so the better.

'You had no right to follow me!'

'My dear Sara,' the deliberate drawl gave the endearment a derogatory sound, 'I don't hold back from doing what I wish.'

The retort which should have been simple, was not simple at all, especially when she was subjected to a scrutiny that was nothing less than outrageous. His gaze lingered a few moments on eyes that were distressed despite all attempts to keep them blank, on lips that trembled, then descended to the swell of the high breasts above the confining limits of the bikini, to waist and hips and thighs. If he had used his hands to tear the brief garment from her body, he could not have undressed her more thoroughly, Sara thought wildly.

As it was, the opportunity for retort slipped by. Instead, when she could speak, Sara asked, 'How did you know where to find me.'

'You left a very clear set of footprints.'

He knew what she was asking, but he was making her spell the words out. He was playing with her. Through the excitement his closeness provoked, Sara was aware of an intense anger.

She wanted to hit him; only a deliberate effort kept her hands at her side. For the action would set forth a chain of consequences over which she would have no control—she was very certain of that.

He was so sure of himself, she thought bitterly. No stranger would have taken him for a doctor on his way to fame. In denim shorts and an open-

necked shirt he could more easily have been a
beachcomber or a surfer. His shirt was open to
just above his waist, so that she could see the mass
of golden hairs that curled on the lean yet well-
muscled chest. His legs were very long, taut and
strong, planted almost aggressively in the soft sand.
He possessed an unrestrained maleness which
played havoc with her frenzied senses.

Involuntarily her eyes moved upwards to his
face. There was no denying that his appearance
was distinguished, but had his face always been
quite so rakish? Had there always been the impression of strength mixed with cruelty in the set of his
lips and the rigid line of his jaw; the look of challenge and devil-may-care in the narrowed ice-blue
eyes?

'How did you know where to find me?' she asked
again, managing somehow to retain her composure. 'You didn't just happen along this beach.
Casual strangers don't come here.'

He shot her a long level look. 'I went to Morning
Glow.'

If only she had given instructions to Lettie to
tell nobody where she was! But after Clyde's obvious astonishment at seeing her yesterday it had not
occurred to her that he would know where she
lived.

'What you're really asking is how I learned about
Morning Glow.'

'Yes. . . .' She did not know that her lips were
white.

The eyes that met hers held an expression of disgust, as if she had committed a crime which he
could not condone. Sara felt a quiver that began at

the base of her spine and travelled swiftly upwards.
She had an inkling of what was coming.

'After I left you,' he said, his words slow and
measured, 'I made some enquiries. I wanted to
know more about the ballet dancer who ran the
village antique shop.'

'You could have asked me,' she said tersely.

'Would you have told me the truth?' His face
totally without emotion. 'What I learned was interesting. Sara Demaine, the dancer who put her
career before all else, had married the famous
choreographer, Peter Burod. The very wealthy
Peter Burod.'

'Yes.'

'. . . and was living at Morning Glow, an estate
worth a fortune.'

'You make it sound so cheap,' she whispered.
'Did you also hear that Peter . . . my husband . . .
was killed in a motor accident?'

'I heard.' Compassion touched his eyes, only to
vanish before she could glean any comfort there-
from.

'I also heard,' he went on, 'that the wealthy
widow chose to continue living at Morning Glow
after her husband's death. That her work in the
antique shop is of a temporary nature. . . .'

'I might decide to put money into the shop,' she
interrupted him, 'to work there full-time.'

The hands that gripped her shoulders caught her
unprepared. Clyde's fingers dug hard into the soft
skin. 'An antique shop, Sara? What are you playing
at, for heaven's sake?'

'I happen to like antiques,' she said defensively.

'I like them too. That's why yesterday. . . .' He

stopped. 'It doesn't make sense. You're a dancer, a damned fine dancer. You broke up with me because you were so obsessed with the idea of a starring role. What happened, Sara?'

Now was the time to tell him. She opened her mouth, only to close it again. Telling Clyde the truth would also mean telling him why she had ended their engagement. Even now, she could not do that.

'Peter asked me to marry him. . . .'

'And you agreed.' She saw the sudden whiteness in his face, the expression that came and went in his eyes, an expression of pain she thought, and briefly her heart went out to him. Clyde thought she had given him up in favour of someone with more to offer. Sara, who had had to endure so much, was able to identify with the pain of another; especially when it was the pain of the man she loved. For she did love him—desperately. Despite the fact that he was married himself. Despite his new feelings of disgust.

'Try to understand. . . .' she began.

'What is there to understand?' he asked through his teeth. The fingers on her shoulders moved upwards towards her neck. There was an urgency in his touch which Sara had never felt before, an urgency that had nothing to do with the passion they had once known, and once more she was frightened.

'Well?' The word was a whiplash.

'Take your hands off my neck,' she said unsteadily.

Clyde's laugh, short and unamused, fanned her ear. 'Scared I'll strangle you?'

'Clyde. . . .'

'You're safe enough.' He dropped his fingers abruptly. 'Did Peter Burod ever get angry with you? Or was he too old for that? Too grateful for a young girl's love.'

'Why do you make it so ugly?' In the aftermath of tension she was trembling.

'Because it is ugly.'

'No!' She took a step away from him and began to walk. There was no point in continuing the conversation.

He fell in beside her. Abstractedly Sara noticed that their shadows were close together; merging now and then. As their bodies had merged once before. And never would again. . . .

'Peter Burod must have been a good thirty years older than you.' Evidently Sara's attempt to end the conversation meant nothing to Clyde.

'Twenty-five.'

'And very rich.'

'He was rich.' She turned suddenly, pausing in mid-step, tilting her head back to look at him. 'What are you trying to prove?'

'That you're a mercenary little bitch.'

'I think you implied something of the sort yesterday.' She was so angry that it was no effort to keep her voice as cool as his.

'And that all your ideals never meant a damn thing.'

Later she would feel pain. When she relived the things they had said to each other. Now there was just the necessity of keeping up a composed front.

Lifting her head, cheeks burning, she said, 'You're entitled to believe what you wish. I don't have to wait around while you do it.'

Pivoting away from him in a dancer's neat movement, she began to walk—quickly, angrily. Until an arm caught her from behind, the hand beneath her breasts jerking the breath from her lungs.

'Let me go!' she muttered through clenched teeth.

'When we've finished talking.' Biting amusement in his tone.

He knows that he's hurting me, Sara thought. And he doesn't care. Perhaps he enjoys it.

'I can't take much more.' Her voice was strangely husky. The look she sent him was one of pleading.

'Not even this?' he queried softly.

She had no chance to escape as he turned her completely and pulled her into his arms. He moved more quickly than she did, so that his mouth found hers before she could twist her head away. For a moment she went quite limp, then she stiffened, forcing her lips to remain closed again the pressure of his kiss.

For so long she had waited for this moment; had woken in the mornings knowing that Clyde had been in her dreams, heavy with the terrible wanting to be in his arms. But this was not the embrace she had longed for. This was a combination of his own hurt and his wish to hurt her. It was cruel and calculating, intending to punish. It was an embrace not to be endured.

'Let me go!' she snapped through clenched teeth when he lifted his head to draw breath.

He held her a little away from him, so that he

could look down into her face. 'Is frigidity another one of your personality changes?'

Was there to be no letting up? The loveliness of the morning had vanished. Sara felt suddenly ill. 'You don't know much about me,' she said.

'You're probably right,' Clyde agreed. 'Though I once thought I did. What I do know—' he paused, eyes narrowed and so speculative that Sara felt herself tense in anticipation of whatever was coming—'is that you can be a very warm-blooded female when you choose.'

He had not forgotten. He remembered every detail of the night when they had made love in his apartment. Just as she did.

'You did turn me on once,' she admitted, her eyes wide and steady despite the contempt in his own expression. 'You don't any longer.'

'Who turns you on these days?' he enquired lazily.

Sara moistened her lips. 'You know that I'm a widow.'

'A very lovely widow, young, desirable.' The corners of his lips lifted just a little. 'In that way at least you haven't changed.'

He still found her desirable. Ridiculous that notwithstanding his taunting that one fact should yet be meaningful. In the small second of joy she understood that an awareness of her feelings would give him even more power over her than he possessed already. Also, that he would not hesitate to use it.

She raised her head, and the glance she threw him was cool and remote. 'Thanks for the compliment—not that it means anything. I can't deny that

I once slept with you. I don't happen to make a habit of it. With Peter dead, I have no desire to sleep with anyone else.'

He was still holding her. Now the hands that were on her back jerked her to him with sudden violence. 'Don't give me that! You never loved him.'

'I loved my husband very much,' Sara said shakily. Clyde need not know that the love she spoke of was not the same as the love she had felt for Clyde himself. 'Nor do I want to discuss him.'

'If I didn't know you better I'd think you were like the swan-maiden you once danced. Pure and sweet, relatively untouched.' His tone was harsh. 'A false image. You married a man for his money and the material things he could give you. You slept with me. And with how many others besides?'

'No others.' She was very white. 'Clyde, please stop, before you say something you'll regret. . . .'

'And now you claim to be content with a celibate life,' he jeered. 'Who is there? Well, Sara?'

It was possible to keep her temper in check just so long. She was no longer thinking as she bent backwards, and struck him hard across the face.

Clyde was white as he touched his cheek. But when he spoke there was an odd satisfaction in his tone. 'I wondered what it would take to shatter that madonna-like façade.'

'You wouldn't believe me,' Sara said, shuddering.

'I still don't. There's passion inside you, Sara Demaine. You could no more live without sex than you could live without food.'

Again he pulled her to him. She could feel the

length of his body against hers as he tightened his hold and crushed her to him. He was as taut and hard as she remembered him. Taut thighs and a hard line of hipbone, and the hardness of a chest in which the heart beat as strongly and rapidly as her own. Hardness of shoulder, where her head had once nestled willingly and now lay under protest. A hardness, which despite the indignation and outrage filling her mind, brought excitement cascading through her nerve-stream in waves of fire.

One hand went to her hair, sliding up her neck to pull it back from her face, then drawing her head back. His lips went to her ears, playing first with one small lobe, then the other, tracing a path across her eyes and around her mouth without resting on her lips. The path of his mouth was tantalising, with none of the brutality his earlier kiss had contained. Sara felt sensuous pleasure that brought a stifled cry to her lips. Somewhere, in the farthest reaches of her mind, was the knowledge that she had to resist him. But the knowledge was rapidly swamped by the desire leaping within her. If she had control left over her reactions, it was only the merest thread.

She felt his tongue trail sensuously down the sensitive column of her throat, then his mouth returned once more to hers. Her own lips parted willingly, for her mind had abandoned the last of its protest. He began a slow exploration of her mouth and she was lost completely. Without thinking, she lifted her arms and caught his head in her hands, letting her fingers bury themselves in the thick soft hair above his ears.

Her response seemed to ignite fresh fires in

Clyde. The increased hardness of his body as he welded her to him revealed that his wanting was as great as her own. One hand went easily beneath the flimsy bikini-bra, curving forward to reach a breast. The soft nipple hardened beneath his touch, so that even if she had been able to maintain an outward control, her body would now have betrayed her.

He lifted his head quite suddenly and stared down at her. His colour was high, his breathing ragged. There was an odd expression in his eyes. If she had not been so dazed by emotion she would have seen it.

As it was, she saw the break in his kisses only as a respite in which she could draw breath and murmur what was on her mind. 'Clyde, not here. . . . Someone might come along . . . see us. . . .'

'Then you do intend to sleep with me.'

She was caught not so much by the words as by the tone. For a moment she stared at him un-comprehendingly. It took several seconds before reality struck. Clyde had made love to her for a purpose. He had taunted her about her façade of purity and untouchability. He had spoken of it with contempt. As the expression in his eyes began to register, she understood it for what it was. Understood too that he had had a purpose in making love to her.

'You . . . you aroused me deliberately!' Her voice was shaking.

'Perhaps I did.' The acknowledgement came quietly. 'And in your own way you asked for it.' He paused, watching her all the time. Then he said, 'You must have known I'd come looking for you, no matter your protests of surprise. That's why you wore this bikini. You'd have remembered it turned me on once before.'

Sara was past caring, past noticing. 'Leave me, Clyde. Just leave me.' Her eyes were bright with unshed tears.

His hands dropped to his side. 'It's not what you want.'

'You don't know the first thing about what I want!'

'You need a man, Sara.'

'But not you! Anyone but you!' She turned to face the ocean, knowing that she could not hold the tears back much longer, knowing that she did not want him to see them, unaware that he had seen them already.

'Thank God I won't have to see you again,' she said tersely. 'Your life is in Cape Town. Mine is here.'

'Mine is here too,' he said very quietly.

Forgetting her tears, she spun round at the unexpected rejoinder. 'You don't mean that!'

'I have an appointment at Stellenberg.'

She gazed at him speechlessly. He looked back at her, registering her shock. Something flickered in the blue eyes, then, without another word of explanation, he turned on his heel and walked away in the opposite direction from the one he had come.

Sara watched him go. His stride was loose and supple. From the back even more than from the front, he did not look like a doctor. The shock of fair hair, blown by the wind, and the bronzed

limbs, long and well-shaped and muscular, gave
him the appearance of one whom an artist would
wish to immortalise in paint or marble.

Sara herself was as still as any statue. Just
minutes ago, when her body had trembled with
arousal, she had felt as if she was on fire. Now,
although the sky burnt down from an African sky
that was vast and blue and cloudless, she was
gripped by a great chill.

Clyde here. Living here, working here. Her mind
rejected the fact, even while she knew she must find
a way of accepting it. Clyde *could not* live here. His
life was in Cape Town; that was where he must
stay. Loving him had brought her to the edges of
despair once—admittedly through no fault of his.
She never wanted to experience that kind of unhappiness again.

Sara knew about Stellenberg. It was a hospital
for ill children, mainly children who had been
crippled. Morning Glow was situated a little way
west of the village, Stellenberg some ten miles east.
Sara had never been there; she was not acquainted
with any of the children who lived there. The death
of her own baby was still so recent as to make her
unhappy in the presence of other children, especially sick ones. Their misfortune would touch her
beyond endurance.

What she knew of the home was through Peter.
He had talked highly of Stellenberg. But he had
never spoken of Clyde in the context of the place.
Either he had wanted to spare her—if her erstwhile
fiancé had not been mentioned between them, her
husband had nevertheless understood that her feelings for him had not vanished—or Clyde's ap-

pointment was recent.

That he should be there at all was a puzzle. It did not fit in with Sara's image of what Clyde Montgomery wanted of life. Of what Andrea would want for him. Perhaps, she thought, a few months at the home might be part of some compulsory practical training. There were children at the home who would need surgery, and Clyde could help them.

The lithe figure had grown small with distance. He must have walked half a mile by now, Sara thought, and seemed to be making toward one of the holiday beaches. How he would get his car back from Morning Glow, if that indeed was how he had come there, she did not know, did not care. She herself would slip back in through a side entrance that was concealed from the front of the house.

Not once had Clyde turned back. Had he done so he might have seen the small slight figure who watched him, eyes never leaving him for a second. He had become one with the blur of golden sand when Sara finally began to retrace her steps. For the first time she saw the footprints that ran alongside her own—bigger prints, forming a parallel line with hers.

The tide had risen in the time since she had walked this way. The water left by the incoming waves washed over the footprints, leaving a curving mark on the sand some inches beyond them. Here and there, where a print was especially deep, a little of the foam remained. Soon there would be nothing left of the parallel prints, Sara knew. There was something symbolic in the fact. In just this way her

relationship with Clyde had been a temporary
thing. It seemed only fitting that the visible sign of
their togetherness today was temporary also.

With the rising of the tide the sound of the surf
had increased. It was more difficult to negotiate
the way back, for there were parts where rocks
which had previously been exposed were now slip-
pery with water. Sara had to tread warily. But she
was not frightened. For all her outward frailty, she
could cope with the elements of nature.

It was a situation with which she did not know
how to cope, a situation and a set of facts.

How would she handle things next time she met
Clyde? There was no doubt in her mind that the
probability of a next time existed. While she had
closeted herself at Morning Glow her contact with
people had been limited. Clyde could have been at
Stellenberg some months. He might have shopped
in the village, eaten with Andrea in a restaurant.
Sara would not have known. Lettie had been in
the habit of doing the shopping; Sara herself had
seldom gone into the village.

Now all was changed. She was obligated to
Lynn. Her friend had worked very hard to make
the Antique Den a profitable enterprise. She had
taken the cruise with her mother only because she
knew that her business was in good hands. There
was no way Sara could decide to stop running the
shop. She could not let Lynn down.

Nor did she want to let Lynn down, she decided.
Her friend had been right about one thing: for too
long she had made Morning Glow a retreat, a
prison, a comfortable hideaway where she was
sheltered from life and its demands. It was time

that she broke free of the chains she had forged for herself, no matter that pain might be involved. If she was to build a new life for herself—as she *must* do, she told herself firmly—then self-respect had to be an integral part of it. There could be no self-respect while she remained in hiding.

With the wind blowing her hair, and the surf roaring, and the gulls soaring and dipping over the waves, Sara was able to be honest with herself. Part of her reluctance to return to Cape Town had stemmed from the fear that some time she might meet Clyde. She had met him anyway. In the village the chances of meeting him were almost inevitable.

She would have to learn to deal with such a meeting. Once she had had the strength to push herself to the limits of her physical endurance. For the sake of her career she had driven herself to dance when her aching muscles screamed to her to stop. Now she must push herself to accept a situation. She could not run away—she *would not*. She owed something to Lynn. Even more she owed something to herself.

It would not be easy to meet Clyde, to talk with him just as she would with anyone else. It would be even less easy to see him with Andrea. Yet that too was inevitable. She must be ready for the situation when it arose.

She lifted her head, welcoming the spray that moistened her cheeks, the freshness of the sea air, the taste and smell of salt. Her step quickened. She was letting memories and the force of Clyde's personality get to her unnecessarily. For reasons of his own he had decided to seek her out today. Although she would have said that Clyde was a person who would force himself to shunt the past out of his system and concentrate on the present, perhaps the matter of hurt male pride had never been entirely resolved. He might have followed her this morning with the sole purpose of proving something—what exactly? she wondered—both to her and to himself.

One thing was fact: Clyde was married. As such any further meetings would be purely coincidental. Neither he nor Andrea would wish it otherwise. Just as she herself did not wish it, Sara told herself. And wondered why a small voice deep inside her whispered denial.

CHAPTER SIX

THE next days were so busy that Sara had little time to think of Clyde. It was the holiday season, and custom was brisk. It appeared that Lynn had a flair for searching out the unusual. People were attracted to the Antique Den in much the same way as Sara had seen them attracted to Lynn herself. Slowly but surely it was becoming a name to be remembered among those who liked quality combined with something out of the ordinary. Sara had been shocked by Clyde's visit to the shop. Now, remembering his penchant for old things, she understood that his visit could have been only a matter of time.

It was hard to push Clyde from her mind completely. Sara wondered if the time would come when she would ever be able to do that. There was more to it than that he had been the first man she had slept with, and that he was the only man she had ever loved crazily and with an utter lack of reserve. It seemed that he had become a part of her; part of her thinking being, her emotions; part of her very bloodstream. Accepting that, she was yet wise enough to know that she could not let him destroy her, as he would surely do if she allowed him to dominate her every thought and waking minute. She must make a point of concentrating on other things.

She threw herself into the running of the Antique Den with all the energy which had been pent up inside her for too long. She did most of the serving herself. Lynn had given her the name of a girl who was willing to assist whenever necessary, but Sara called on her only rarely. She made it her business to find out as much as she could about each article in the shop, and was filled with pride when she found herself able to discuss a purchase intelligently with a customer.

The more Sara immersed herself in antiques, the more fascinated she became. There was so much to learn, to know. There were the important periods in European furniture and styles; Regency and Chippendale, Queen Anne and Georgian. There were dynasties in Oriental culture when objects of priceless value had been produced. Ming and Wan Li and Sung became names with meaning. There was so much to learn, to know. It was not enough that Sara should be able to pick up an object and quote a price. She wanted to be able to talk with customers from a position of strength, or at least on equal terms.

In the evenings, she sat in the library at Morning Glow and read. Disregarding Lettie's clucks of disapproval, 'Miss Sara will get sick again, and then where will we be?' she read till the early hours of the morning. She was learning that Africa had a culture all its own. Just as the lovely gabled houses were products of Cape Dutch architecture, so there was furniture that was uniquely of Cape craftsmanship. Furniture in woods that were unknown in Europe; stinkwood and kiaat and a particular rich-looking mahogany. There were objects of silver, the Cape silver which Clyde had asked to see. Lovely things that were becoming increasingly valuable and hard to find.

As one piece of knowledge led to another, Sara found new avenues of knowledge to explore. She was learning more of the history of the African continent. She went to the library and looked for books, and she realised that there was a whole area of knowledge which she had never known existed. Once ballet had encompassed her world. When that had been taken from her, she had felt empty. The Antique Den had introduced her to a new world, one that was interesting and exciting in an entirely different way. It was a world which she felt she might very well wish to make her own.

If the reading increased her knowledge, it also kept her from dwelling on Clyde. At night, when she was asleep, Sara was powerless to control her dreams. In the mornings she would waken with memories that were sometimes too painfully vivid. This was not new. She had dreamed of Clyde even when she had been married to Peter. She could only hope that with time her subconscious mind would relinquish what seemed an obsession.

But at least her conscious mind was under control—much of the time anyway. When she found herself thinking of Clyde she would firmly change the drift of her thoughts. Hard though that was, more and more she was successful.

Lynn had given her authority to attend auctions and sales, and had told her how much she could spend.

'If I go, I might buy the wrong things,' Sara had protested.

Lynn had laughed. 'If you don't go, you could slip up on something we ought to have.'

'You'd really trust me,' Sara had said wonderingly.

'I trust your gut instincts.' There had been a perceptive glance from candid eyes. 'You'll be okay.'

On a Saturday, just a week after the encounter with Clyde, Sara went to a sale. She had taken an inland road to the farmhouse some thirty miles from Morning Glow. Coming back, with a trunkfull of first-edition leather-bound books, she took the road that paralleled the sea, and was rounding a bend when she saw Stellenberg.

The sight was a shock. Momentarily the car jerked. Sara was aware of the tension knotting her neck and her shoulders, and when she looked at the wheel she saw that her knuckles were white.

Her first instinct was to drive on, when she saw a widening in the road, a viewpoint where cars could pause to admire a particularly lovely view of the bay. She pulled off the road and drew the vehicle to a halt. Deliberately, very deliberately, she forced herself to relax, first one set of muscles then another, till all of her body was at ease. Then she looked once more at Stellenberg.

Like so many of the houses in the Cape Peninsula, its architecture was Cape Dutch. There were the lovely gables, the brown-shuttered windows, the graceful pillars at the front of the stoep. There were the white walls covered with creepers, a wide expanse of lawn bordered with the indigenous aloes and proteas. In the shade of some trees was a group of children. Sara saw that many were in wheelchairs.

Clyde was nowhere in sight, and Sara was glad of the fact. She would not have wanted him to see her, to wonder what had brought her to this spot. She was not certain herself why she was here.

She had had no conscious intention of driving past Stellenberg. Yet in the inner reaches of her mind perhaps, there had been the need to see the place where Clyde worked, where he lived. A little despairingly she wondered whether there would always be the sense of wanting to know where he was and what he was doing. Whether he was fulfilled, happy. . . .

Was that what loving a person was all about? Was it an emotion that remained locked in one's heart long after any hope of a future had vanished? She tried to tell herself that she could not, would not, be forever haunted by thoughts of the man she had so nearly married. Somewhere there must be a man who could make her forget. Yet Peter Burod, with all the love and kindness and humanity that was in him, had not succeeded. Did the man exist who could?

Curiously she looked at the gabled house on the forested slope. She would not have pictured it as a setting for a man of Clyde's ambitions. As before, she wondered too about Andrea. She was unable to visualise Clyde's wife as being anything but restless on this wild and lonely stretch of coast.

Or was just being with Clyde enough for Andrea? Did she love him so much that loneliness ceased to matter? If that were so, Sara would be able to understand.

A lump came into her throat as she realised how close she had been to living here herself. The thought was unbidden, involuntary; it was hard to push away all the same. Only a conversation over-heard in a shrub-covered arbour had set her life in a different direction. As Clyde's wife, entitled to witness his work and share his dreams, she would have walked with him along the beach in the even-ings. She would have lain in his arms at night, lis-tening as he talked of healing sick children. And later, when they had said all they wanted, there would have been loving. . . .

She did not know that her eyes were wet till her hand brushed against her cheek and felt a tear. This would never do! She had resolved to put Clyde out of her mind. If she could not stamp out her love for him, at least she must remember not to think of him. She swallowed, blew her nose, then turned the key in the ignition. Jerkily she guided the car back on to the tar.

She spent the afternoon at the shop working on the books she had bought. Lynn would be pleased with the purchase, she knew, as she went through them. Not every book was worth keeping, but among them were a few that made up for the rest. One in particular, an account of the Cape hinter-land by an eighteenth-century traveller, had Sara enthralled.

It was only as she drove back to Morning Glow that her mind returned to Clyde. Sadness filled her once more but with it came a feeling of pride. She had managed to concentrate solely on her work. For a few hours no other thoughts had intruded.

Clyde and her dancing—two loves that had once been all her world. Both would be a part of her always, but at least the last days had shown her that she was able to make a new life for herself. If it was not the life she would have chosen, she understood more and more that it could be a satisfying one nonetheless. It rested with her to make it so.

On Sunday morning Sara stood at the window of her room and looked over the lawns to the sea. She was strangely restless. Lately her life had taken on new purpose. On weekdays she woke up each morning knowing that she had to be at the shop in time to open the door. It was a satisfying feeling. Today she had nothing to do.

The sky was blue and cloudless, a perfect day for sunbathing. But she had no desire to go to the sands. Since her encounter with Clyde, she had not walked on the beach. Notwithstanding her resolve to be strong, she was reluctant to relive memories that were still very raw.

Frowning, she turned from the window. It was more than a year since she had been in Cape Town. She would go there today. There were friends she had not seen for too long. Running the Antique Den was her first step back towards independence. It was time she went further.

She spent a few moments at the open doors of her wardrobe before deciding on a turquoise slacks suit. The outfit was one of her favourites. Contrasting vividly with glossy dark hair and honey-skinned face, the deep pastel shade heightened an appearance that was exotic yet ethereal. Going back to the world that had once been hers, even if only for a day, should not require an act of courage —but it did. The knowledge that she was looking her best was reassuring.

She did not go directly to the garage, but walked instead to the edge of the lawn, pausing at the top of the path that led down to the beach. A haze hung over the water, so that there was no horizon to mark the line between sea and sky. There was no wind, the water was tranquil. The sand was smooth and untrodden. Involuntarily almost, Sara recalled a set of footprints, parallel-going, one set small and high-stepped, the other deep and large. Abruptly she turned away. Today was not for memories; it was for a fresh start.

Quickly she made her way to the garage. The path she took did not go past the front of the house, so that she did not see the low-slung grey car parked on the drive. The sound of the sea had drowned out its approach.

She was at the door of her own car, her fingers about to turn the key, when a voice said from behind her, 'Going somewhere?'

Shock quivered through her. For a long moment she stood very still, not turning, giving herself time to regain her composure.

When she did turn it was slowly, deliberately. With a steadiness she was far from feeling, she said, 'I'm going to Cape Town.'

'Any special reason?'

His tone was casual, deceptively casual, Sara knew. Clyde had not driven to Morning Glow

merely to engage her in small-talk. She felt her
muscles tensing inside her.

'Visiting friends.'

'Go another day.'

She looked at him, and then away. Each time
she saw him his maleness came as a fresh shock.
Though she tried to harden herself against his
impact, her senses responded instinctively to the
vital attractiveness of him. Just one moment had
been enough to take in the long strong line of his
jaw, the gauntness of high cheekbones, eyes that
were too perceptive, and lips that were mobile and
sensuous. There was too much pleasure in the
memory of what those lips could do.

'No,' she said as firmly as she could. Deliberately
she turned back to the car, made her fingers move
to the keys. 'If you'll excuse me. . . .'

'I didn't come all this way to do that.' Still the
same easy tone. 'You're coming with me, Sara.'

She swung round. No matter how much she
wanted to go with him—God, how much she
wanted that! despite the fact that she did not even
know where he intended taking her—she was
outraged that he imagined she would automatically
fall in with his whims.

'You couldn't have heard me,' she said icily. 'I'm
visiting friends.'

'I heard you. I also know that you made no prior
arrangements.' The corners of his mouth lifted in a
smile. 'I gathered from your housekeeper that your
trip is impromptu.'

It was the unexpectedness of the smile that was
her undoing. It was such a long time since she had
seen it. When she said, 'I *am* going to Cape Town,'

she knew that her hesitation had not gone un-
noticed.

'Another time.' His gentleness was as unexpected
as the smile. 'We're wasting the day, Sara. Put your
keys back in your bag and let's go.'

She could feel her anger slipping from her. In
this mood he was too hard to resist. 'You're a very
autocratic man,' she commented, as he started the
engine of his own car.

'If you thought that when you first knew me,
you never mentioned it.' His tone was light.

'I was polite.' A swift glance at the strong face
told her he knew she was lying. In those first rapturous weeks, when she had been in love with a
passion she had never dreamed possible, she had
not once thought him arrogant. She had not seen
in him any of the qualities she was to glimpse
later—contempt, hardness, an ability to hurt.
Then, in those golden weeks when they had spoken
openly of their love, she had seen only strength
combined with a wonderful tenderness.

The strength was there still, every line of his
face, his body, evidenced that. As for tenderness—
that would be reserved for Andrea, for his wife.
The thought brought pain stabbing sharp inside
her.

'So you were polite. Did it ever occur to you,
Sara, that there were qualities you hid from me
when we met?'

No need to ask what he meant. It was clear that
he thought the worst of her, yet she could not
defend herself without telling him the truth. The
chance to do that had vanished long ago. Even if
she did tell him—and the temptation existed—the

ensuing conversation would open up other truths:
the loss of their baby, her illness, the knowledge
that she could never dance again. Tragedies which
she was just beginning to accept in her own mind.
She could talk about these things to Lynn, the
friend who understood what she had gone through.
She could not talk of them to Clyde, for after the
initial disbelief would come pity, and that she
would be unable to endure.

'Well, Sara?'

She looked at him, eyes stark with unhappiness.
'Perhaps it's human nature to show one's best side,
especially when . . .'—the words were hard to get
out—'when one is in love.'

'So you did love me?' There was a strange inflection in his voice.

She kept her eyes on the road. 'Yes. I . . . I never
lied about that. Clyde, can we change. . . .'

'But you discovered that you loved your career
even more,' he cut in relentlessly.

'Yes.' This time it was easier to reply.

'And that was all-important until you were faced
with the temptation of great wealth and a famous
name.'

With what ease he had lured her into a trap! A
retort was on the tip of her tongue, but somehow
she managed to bite it back. Just a few moments
ago she had decided that there was no way she
would tell Clyde the truth, and the knowledge did
nothing to soften her anger and humiliation.

'You know all the answers,' she said very quietly.
'I said just now that you were autocratic. You are
also arrogant and a bastard. Let me out, Clyde.'

'No.'

His mouth was set, she saw, and knew there was no point in arguing with him. It was clear that he would not stop the car, and for her to try to open her door would be as foolhardy as it would be melodramatic. She had no choice at all but to stay where she was, and it came to her that some irrational part of her was excited to be a captive passenger. The knowledge gave her no happiness.

'You haven't told me where you're taking me.'

'Stellenberg.'

'Oh!' She should not have been surprised, but oddly she was. 'Clyde, why?'

A pair of intelligent eyes, blue as the sky and as distant, were turned briefly on her. 'I want you to see it.'

'Why?' she asked again.

'Because it's time that you saw another side of life.'

Sara stared at him wordlessly a long moment. If he had said merely that he wanted her to see the place where he worked, that would have meant much to her. As it was, there seemed no end to the pain he wanted to inflict on her.

His concentration was on the road once more when she said, 'Andrea won't like it.'

She told herself that it was only in her imagination that she felt the car jerk. It could have been nothing else, for a split second later it was purring as sleekly as ever over the tar. Once more Clyde turned his head. Something glimmered in his eyes, an expression Sara could not define. As his gaze rested on her face, Sara felt her muscles bunch inside her.

He shrugged. 'Andrea won't mind.'

He gave his attention back to the road. Sitting as far away from him as she could, Sara studied his profile. The determined line of the chin, the strong nose, the hair that curled around his ears to lie against the crisp collar of his shirt. His head was easily erect, the set of his lips relaxed. His hands on the wheel were the sensitive hands of a doctor, hands that healed. They were also the hands of a lover. Once they had stirred Sara to an ecstasy which she knew she would never experience with another man. Now these hands would give pleasure to his wife.

His wife. . . . So Andrea wouldn't mind Sara's coming to Stellenberg with Clyde. It could only mean that she was now so secure in her relationship with her husband that his renewed acquaintance with an erstwhile fiancée did not threaten her at all.

They were still some distance from Stellenberg. Sara turned to the window. There had been a few moments today when she had been so swept with the joy of being alone with Clyde, that she had forgotten that he was married. Sitting beside him there had been memories of other drives. Then she had been close to him, not huddled against her door. There had been a lovely ease between them, laughter and talking and endearments. And when silence had fallen it had been the comfortable silence of two people who understood each other.

If only Clyde had not re-entered her life, she wished now. To some extent the memories had faded in the two years since she had seen him. There had been so much else to occupy her mind—

the death of her baby, and then of Peter; the break with her dancing. Now, with Clyde just inches from her, the memories had been awakened with as much vividness as if the events themselves had only just taken place.

She tried to focus her attention on the scenery beyond the road, but awareness of the long hard body behind the steering-wheel made concentration difficult. The road was part of the lovely coastal stretch called the Garden Route. Each twist and bend gave on to breathtaking vistas. On one side, dropping steeply away from the edge of the kerb, was the sea, a study in blues ranging from turquoise to deepest Prussian. There were narrow inlets and tiny coves and lagoons which cut through the land to the water. On the other side of the road were mountains; rugged-faced slopes giving way to lush forests treed with timber from which costly furniture was made—stinkwood, kiaat and yellow-wood.

One could never tire of the beauty, Sara had often thought in the past. Yet today, much as she tried, the loveliness was no more than a blur before her eyes. In sharper focus, despite the fact that she had turned away from him, were Clyde's lean features. Every inch of his face was engraved upon her mind with the clarity of a photograph. There would never be a time when she would need pictures to remind her of Clyde, Sara knew, and wished that she could banish him from her consciousness now, even for just a few minutes.

The enforced proximity was dangerous, wrecking her peace of mind and doing alarming things to her senses. She ached with the longing to move

across the seat, to lean against him, arm brushing
arm, thigh lying against thigh, head resting against
the hardness of his shoulder. As that could not be
she wished they would come quickly to Stellenberg.
She had to get out of the car and away from an
atmosphere that threatened to overpower her with
its sensuousness and sexual tension.

CHAPTER SEVEN

STELLENBERG was all that Peter had described it, and more. As Clyde showed her around, Sara was struck by the airy brightness of the place. There was suffering here, and pain. But there was also peace and serenity.

There were children of all ages, many of them in wheelchairs. Sara was filled with compassion as she walked past them. At the same time she realised that her dread of coming here had been unjustified. The atmosphere at Stellenberg was not one of despair but rather of hope. The children seemed to have an eagerness common to all children. They did not seek her pity, Sara realised. They wanted to be treated as normally as possible.

Which was what Clyde did. Sara followed quietly as he led her from one group to another. From the moment that she had learned where he worked, she had found it hard to believe that with his ambitions he would be content for long in a place so far removed from the nerve-centres of medicine—the hospitals of the big cities. Though she had not yet asked him the question, she had been certain that his position could only be temporary. And yet, as she watched Clyde with the children, she was struck by his manner. Something about it spoke of permanence, of a deep attachment for this home where so many children were helped. Sara was not sure why she felt quite so moved.

He knew each child by name. He seemed to be

acquainted with their anxieties and their interests. He had time to spare for all of them. A boy, his leg in a cast, was having trouble assembling a model plane. Clyde helped him, but only as much as the boy wanted, Sara noticed. A little girl was writing a letter; when she saw Clyde she asked him the spelling of a word.

The children called him Dr Clyde. Sara saw smiles when he came near and eyes that brightened. One child threw her arms about his neck and hugged him. The affection was a lovely thing to see, it was deep and spontaneous.

Once, a long time ago, so it seemed, Sara had thought of Clyde as a man possessed of force of character and authority, a man with charisma and great personal charm. In his lovemaking there had been gentleness coupled with passion.

The discovery that he could also be arrogant was recent. Just today she had called him autocratic and a bastard. Now, as he moved among the children, a new aspect of his personality was revealed, a dedication she had not suspected. It was hard to reconcile this quality with the man who had said his ambitions were to become rich and famous, and who had married the one girl who could further his desires.

It came to Sara that Clyde Montgomery was totally committed to his work, not for the fame that he might achieve, but for the healing he could effect. The compassion and affection he revealed were not assumed; if they had been she would have seen through the deception. In the last two years Clyde had changed even more than she had realised. Unbidden came the wondering whether

Andrea had had something to do with the change.

Questions tumbled on her lips, but she could not frame them. She had thought she knew Clyde as well as one person could know another. The last weeks had shown her that she did not know him at all.

But there was one question she did need to ask. 'Clyde, where is Andrea?'

He looked at her, and the tenderness she had seen in his face a moment ago was gone. 'In Cape Town.'

'For the day?'

His eyes narrowed, as if he resented her persistence. 'I don't know how long she'll be there,' he answered abruptly.

Sara was quiet as they walked on. Had Andrea, disliking the solitude of Stellenberg, decided on a holiday alone? Or had she merely gone back for a visit? Something in Clyde's face seemed to forbid further questions. In any event, the reason for Andrea's absence did not concern Sara. Andrea was Clyde's wife, and as such she would be back. That she was not here today was a relief. It made the visit a little less strained.

'Dr Clyde!'

Sara turned, caught by the sweetness of the voice. In the mauve shade of a jacaranda, a little girl sat in a wheelchair. Green eyes peeped from a small heart-shaped face framed with dark curls, and a small rosebud mouth was curved in a smile. She was the prettiest child she had ever seen, Sara thought, and also the most fragile.

'Jenny love!' exclaimed Clyde. He put his hand on Sara's elbow as they walked to the wheelchair.

'Sara, I want you to meet one of my special people.'

'Hello, Jenny.' Despite the tingling that shot from her arm to her throat, Sara's voice was steady. 'What a lovely place to sit. You can see for miles from here.'

'Dr Clyde says if my eyes were strong enough I could see across the water to Table Mountain,' the child said gravely. She could be ten years old, Sara thought, although at first glance she looked no more than eight. 'Are you Dr Clyde's friend too?'

'I am.' The words came out with surprising ease.

'I love Dr Clyde,' Jenny said.

As I love him, thought Sara. Despite the fact that he doesn't even like me very much any longer.

'It seems he loves you too,' she said gently. And then, looking down at the book on the little girl's lap, 'What are you reading?'

'*The Secret Garden*. It's the fourth time I'm reading it. Have you read it?'

'I have,' Sara said. She was about to ask Jenny what other books she enjoyed, When Clyde cut in with, 'Why don't you tell Mrs Burod what you like best of all, Jenny?'

'I like ballet.'

'Ballet?' Sara suppressed a quiver.

'I just adore ballet.'

Jenny's eyes were dreamlike, as if she witnessed some inner vision which she alone could see. Sara glanced from her to Clyde. His expression was relaxed, but she thought the eyes that met hers held a challenge.

He turned back to Jenny. 'Did you know that

Mrs Burod is a ballet dancer?' he asked, very
casually.

'Honest?' There was sudden radiance in the tiny
white face.

'I was a ballet dancer, once. . . .' Sara said unsteadily.

'Her name was Sara Demaine,' Clyde went on,
addressing himself directly to the child. 'She danced
with a company in Cape Town.'

'Oh!' A breath of pure rapture.

'Clyde, please. . . .' Sara put an instinctive hand
on his arm. A muscle stiffened beneath her fingers.

'Remember the story of *Swan Lake*?' His voice
had not changed. 'The lovely maidens who were
turned into swans?'

'My very favourite!'

'Mrs Burod once danced Odette and Odile, the
good swan and the wicked one.'

'Oh, Mrs Burod!' Jenny's face was brilliant. 'I
never thought I'd meet a real ballet dancer!'

'And now you have,' Sara said gently.

She looked up at Clyde. His eyes had left the
child and were on herself now, studying her with
an intensity that was infinitely disturbing. It was
only with an effort of will that Sara managed to
prevent the trembling that seized her whole body
from becoming visible.

Turning back to the child, she said, 'I could let
you see some of my books. Would you like that,
Jenny?'

'Oh yes!' The little girl pushed herself up in the
wheelchair. 'Do you know we're having a concert?
Dr Clyde, can Mrs Burod dance for us?'

'Why don't you ask her?' Clyde suggested.

'Will you, Mrs Burod? Please . . . please will you dance?'

There was silence as Sara struggled to find an answer. A silence that seemed to transcend the distant crash of the waves. You led me into this deliberately, Clyde, Sara thought. Quite deliberately. You knew the impact this lovely sick child would have on me. You knew that I would find it almost impossible to say no.

Clyde's eyes had never looked so blue, so clear; his face had never been quite so impassive. The blood had drained from her face as she sent him a look of pleading. His only response was a slight shrug.

It was clear that he would not help her. There had been many times in the past weeks when he had angered her. Through it all, incredibly, she had continued to love him. For the first time she felt real hatred.

She bent back to the child. 'I'm sorry, Jenny.'

'Please, Mrs Burod. I've never seen a ballet dancer, not a real one. Please, please dance!'

'I don't dance any more, Jenny.'

'Just this once!'

If pleading was enough to weaken the will, this child possessed an eloquence which could do it. About to agree, Sara recalled the doctor's warning. She would be all right just as long as she did not dance.

'No, Jenny. You'll have a lovely concert, I know.' She put her hand to a cheek that was as frail as old parchment. 'You won't even miss me.'

'Dr Clyde, Won't *you* ask her?' Jenny's persistence was unexpected.

'If you couldn't persuade her, Jenny love, I don't

think I can.' His voice was hard.

Sara could take no more—the little girl's heart-rending loveliness, Clyde's contempt, the trap into which he had led her. She could hardly trust herself to speak as she stood up.

'Goodbye, Jenny,' she managed to get out, then turned from the chair.

If Clyde called after her, she did not hear him. Blindly she walked across the lawn, oblivious of the eyes of children she had spoken to, of the interested glances of the nurses. Some restraint kept her progress to a walk while she was in the grounds of Stellenberg. When she reached the road she began to run.

The road was a sand one, and remained so to the point where it connected with the main road. Her feet in their open-toed sandals were quickly covered with a fine golden dust, but she did not notice it. Once she brushed a hand across her cheek to push away some hair that had blown forward on to her face, and found her cheek wet. She had not even known that she was crying.

This morning there had been joy in the thought of spending a day in Clyde's company, of seeing the place where he worked. Now there was only a desire to put as much distance as possible between herself and Stellenberg. Much as the place had moved her, she knew she would never go there again. If only she could be as certain that she would not see Clyde again!

Twice at the sound of a car coming down the road she flattened herself against the bushes. A truck drew to a halt, and a freckled-faced man offered her a lift. She had to turn his way to refuse,

and saw the oddness of his expression. It came to
her that he had seen her tears and wondered what
a strange weeping girl was doing on a lonely farm-
road.

When another car approached from behind Sara
veered automatically to the side. This time she kept
her face averted. With her tear-stained dishevelled
appearance she would be an oddity to most passers-
by.

The car stopped, violently. Sara was suddenly
scared. As a door opened and feet strode across
the pebbles, she made for a gap between two spiky
cacti. The hand that seized her arm, pulling her
back, had no softness in it. As she was jerked
against a hard body her arm tore against one of
the spikes, but Sara hardly noticed the pain. It was
only part of a far greater pain.

'So you're a coward as well!'

Tears trembling on her lashes, she looked up at
Clyde. 'What do you mean?'

He let his gaze linger on her deliberately, taking
in the tear-filled eyes, the wet cheeks, the little
hollow at the back of her throat where a pulse beat
a feverish tatoo. If he felt any sympathy for her
obvious distress, he did not show it.

'We'll talk in the car.'

'I'm not coming with you.'

'Yes. You're a mess, Sara.'

'That shouldn't matter to you,' she said bitterly.
'I can have a bath when I get back to Morning
Glow.'

'There's no bus.'

'I'll walk. I was walking now.'

'You'd have to pass through the village. The

mistress of Morning Glow with dirty feet and untidy hair!' He laughed harshly. 'My sense of ironic justice might just let you do it.' And then, on another note, 'Get into the car. It's very hot. And since you gave up your dancing you're in no condition to walk all that way.'

His hand was still on her arm, sending shock ripples through her system. In Sara's chest there was an agonising tightness. But she still had her pride. Lifting her head, she said, 'I don't intend coming with you. Not now, not ever again. I can't bear to be near you, Clyde.'

She heard the small hissing intake of breath, and saw a muscle tighten in the long line of his jaw. 'Is that why you're responding to me?'

Her slight flinching movement was involuntary, and quickly controlled, but the curve of his lips showed that it had not escaped him.

'You make a bad liar,' he said, on a note of satisfaction. 'Your body betrays you every time.'

She was still pulling away from him when he scooped her against him and dumped her, with no gentleness, in the car. The few moments in his arms, unloverlike as they had been, had sent new torrents rushing through her. There was something wrong with her, she told herself despairingly, as the long lean body settled itself beside her. Just a few minutes ago she had felt only hatred for him—still did, in fact. The physical desire that had built up inside her made no sense at all.

Somehow she had to break the tension. If conversation was the way to do it she must talk, no matter that Clyde might respond in a manner which would give her no joy.

'You said I was a coward,' she ventured.

'Yes.' Short. Sharp. He too was gripped by an emotion of his own, Sara saw, and put down his feelings to anger.

'Because I went off without waiting for you?'

'That too.' His eyes as they skimmed her held a contempt which was becoming rapidly familiar. 'Mainly because you can't face reality.'

'You've no basis for such a statement,' Sara said unsteadily.

'Haven't I?' His tone was harsh. 'Jenny is a very sick girl—even you must have sensed that. Perhaps you may have realised that she might not have long to live.'

'No!' The exclamation emerged on an outdrawn breath of pain.

Ignoring her protest, he went on. 'You have your own reasons for denying her the pleasure of seeing you dance. But why run away? What is there in your make-up, Sara, that won't allow you to accept the unpleasant things in life?' He paused, and studied her thoughtfully for a moment. 'Do you think sadness is only for other people?'

Sara felt something harden inside her. Clyde had no right to hurt her at every opportunity. It was hurt she felt now—a hurt that was for the lovely child she had left, and for her own child which she had lost, and for a love which became increasingly hard to live with. But he was not going to see her hurt, for this new Clyde would take pleasure in his power and twist the knife further.

Pride, as well as a determination not to let Clyde destroy her, came to her rescue, and she lifted her chin and met his gaze defiantly. 'You don't know

the first thing about it. Do you think I've never
been touched by sadness?'

'Have you?'

There had been moments at which she could
have told him the truth. This was one of them. But
she could not do it. She was overwrought right
now, in a state where her emotions could quite
easily rule her mind.

Forcing a brittle lightness she was far from feeling, she said, 'What an infantile question for a
doctor! Everyone is touched by sadness now and
then.'

'Care to tell me about your particular sadness?'

For the moment the contempt was gone, and in
its place was a thoughtfulness which was nearly
Sara's undoing. Careful, she told herself. Be very
careful.

She shrugged, keeping her face expressionless.
'Nothing out of the ordinary to tell. I was just
stating a very general fact.'

'Nothing special, then.' And when she did not
answer, 'When Peter Burod took you to Morning
Glow it was a little like shutting up the proverbial
bird in the golden cage. I wonder if he knew you'd
use the place to cloister yourself from the real
world.'

Any moment now his taunts would make her
lose her temper, and there was no predicting what
she might say. It was time to change the subject.
'You took me to Stellenberg to show me the real
world?'

'I thought it was time you saw another aspect of
life. That you should know something of the pain

and tragedy with which some people have to contend every day.'

'Noble words!' she threw at him, eyes blazing as she was taken by a new spurt of anger. 'And strange ones, coming from you.'

Clyde's eyes had a dangerous glint. 'What the hell do you mean by that?'

Sara was so angry now that the words emerged easily. 'The altruistic doctor dedicating himself to working with sick children. That role might impress others, it certainly doesn't impress me.'

'Why not?' His voice was very quiet.

Only the brilliance in the blue eyes and the whitening around the nostrils revealed the fury she had provoked in him. They were like two combatants in the ring, she thought, each trying to wound the other where the most blood could be drawn. In this case, they were combatants who had once shared a love that had seemed beautiful beyond dreams. Dully Sara wondered whom she was hurting the most, Clyde or herself. But she had to go on.

'Do you remember telling me once that you meant to be rich and famous?'

'Of course,' he said drily. His eyes swept her body slowly, outrageously. 'I also remember the night I said it.'

The night, if he but knew it, when their child had been conceived. It was madness that she ached with the longing to be in his arms again, to experience the joy of being one with him.

Cheeks burning, she said, 'You were on your way to becoming a surgeon. You meant to make your mark in life.'

'Go on.' His tone was remote, his eyes were chips of ice.'

She took a breath. 'Your marriage to Andrea Stanford wasn't exactly a step in the wrong direction.'

Silence followed. Stealing a glance at him, Sara saw that the lean face had become a mask of chiselled bronze, the lines of it starkly defined as if by some impassioned sculptor. Her own anger of a few moments ago was like nothing against his own. Clyde's lips were compressed in a thin hard line, his nostrils were just slightly flared. Yet when he spoke his tone was without any expression.

'You don't pull your punches.'

She could not apologise, not now. 'In that I seem to be like you,' she said brittley. 'Why are you at Stellenberg, Clyde? Is it just a step to acquiring more experience? Those children trust you, they love you. They'll be devastated when you leave.'

'I have no plans to leave Stellenberg.'

She stared at him, her eyes very wide. 'I don't believe that!'

His expression was sardonic. 'Why not?'

'Your . . . your ambitions,' she said uncertainly, feeling all at once a little out of her depth.

'I don't deny that I once had thoughts of material glory. But people change, Sara.'

There was a quiet positiveness in his words. Despite his fury a few moments ago, Sara sensed that her accusation had not disturbed him in the way she had thought it would. He was very sure of himself, she thought.

'People do change,' she said slowly. 'Perhaps I was wrong about you. If so . . . Clyde, you ask me to accept your changes, why can't you accept mine?'

'Because you haven't grown along with them. From being a wonderful artist you've become content to lead a life of pampered idleness.'

'Don't judge me,' Sara said in a low tone. She shifted her eyes to the window, away from Clyde. On no account did she want him to see how his condemnation had affected her.

Then she asked, 'And what about Andrea?'

'What about her?' His tone was flat, as if warning her to desist.

Sara pressed on regardless. 'Has she changed too? I can't believe she's happy with the direction you've taken.'

'You don't even know Andrea.' Clyde's tone had not changed. 'You only met her for a few moments.'

'That's true,' Sara acknowledged. 'But I know about her. I'd have thought Andrea would want something different for you, a position that carries more status and a lot more money than Stellenberg could afford to pay you.'

Clyde did not answer immediately. When he did speak there was the hardness of finality in his tone. 'I make my own decisions, Sara. At all times.'

And in this case the decision concerned devoting his time and energy to the healing of sick children. Looking at him now, Sara was reminded of the man she had seen an hour earlier. The firmness and strength and sheer animal magnetism that were all so much a part of him had been with him then. But as he had moved among the children there had been other qualities too. Sara had noticed a gentleness and a tenderness, a look of intense caring. She had known that the image he presented was not assumed, it was real, and she had been very moved.

For the first time she knew that she had misjudged him, just as he had misjudged her. It was true that he had said he wanted to be rich and famous. It was also true that he had found consolation for a broken heart—if it ever had been broken—in the arms of Andrea Stanford, the one girl whom his family regarded as a 'match'. But these things had happened two years ago, and two years could be a long time in terms of human experience.

Clyde had indeed changed. Somewhere along the way his values had been transformed. He was a doctor in the true sense of the word. There was a depth of caring for his patients which went beyond the sense of duty.

Clyde would not have needed Andrea's influence to have made his mark in the medical world of a big city. Her personality and his competence would have carried him to any heights he desired. Instead he had chosen to make his life at Stellenberg, giving himself to those who perhaps needed him the most. The sudden revelation moved her anew, so that she found tears pricking at her eyes.

'Tell me about Jenny,' she said, in an attempt to hide her emotion.

'Jenny is a very sick little girl. You know that already.'

Briefly Clyde went into the nature of the child's illness. His tone was matter-of-fact, his face without expression. And yet he was not untouched by

Jenny's plight; Sara knew quite certainly that his sorrow matched her own.

'It would have meant so much to her to see you dance,' he said, when he had finished.

A little hopelessly she shook her head. 'Please . . . don't ask me again.'

'Why, Sara? Why?' He leaned towards her and took one of her hands in his. She heard the urgency in his voice. There was nothing matter-of-fact now in his expression. His eyes were on her face, not with the deliberate sensualness he had displayed earlier, but with a curious intensity, as if he was trying to penetrate to the feelings and thoughts that lay beneath the surface.

'I never used to think of you as empty or selfish,' she heard him say. 'Is there a reason why you don't want to dance?'

Sara was frightened. She needed all her composure if she was to stand her ground, and composure was the one thing she did not have right now. It was very hard to think rationally when she was so disturbed by Clyde's nearness.

If only she could look on him purely as a doctor making a request for one of his patients. As it was, his impact on her was one of maleness, of devastating attractiveness. As always she could feel her senses leaping in response. But she could not let herself react to him now. She had to think clearly, for he was getting too dangerously near to the truth.

'Sara?' He was insistent.

She tried to pull her hand away. His grip had not seemed firm, but at her movement it tightened, the fingers biting into the delicate skin on the inner part of her wrist. She wondered if he could feel the erratic beat of her pulse.

'I've given up that part of my life,' she said abruptly. 'I don't want to start again. It would mean practising ... exercises at the barre. I've finished with all that effort.'

'I don't understand you, Sara.' She heard the disgust in his tone. 'This is such a special case. You'd be giving a sick child pleasure. And not just one child—all the children would enjoy watching you.'

'Can't you leave it alone!' she exclaimed through a half-sob. There was just so much she could take. This time despair lent her strength. She pulled at her hand and freed it, then drew it across her eyes in an unhappy gesture.

She wanted to go home. There was nothing left to say between them. She was turning to him when he said, 'You've hurt yourself.'

'No. . . .'

'Yes—your arm.'

Long fingers touched the skin beneath her elbow. She should be used to his touch by now, yet despite herself she shivered. 'I caught it on a cactus,' she said abruptly, remembering. 'I'll be all right.'

'It needs cleaning.'

'I'll do that when I get home.'

'I'll do it for you now.'

'For heaven's sake,' Sara burst out irritably, 'it's only a scratch!'

'It needs attention. These cacti can be poisonous.' Clyde's voice was authoritative. Sara understood that there was no point in arguing with him.

A spare instrument case was on the back seat.

She sat quite still as he opened it. When he touched her arm again, she was ready for him. Not by a flicker did she betray any emotion.

The cut was cleaned and disinfected, and still his fingers remained on her arm. Until now their touch had been the impersonal one of a doctor. Sara could not have pinpointed the moment at which the touch changed. Now, as Clyde's fingers lingered on her skin, there was a slow sensuousness in the movements which sent the blood racing faster through her veins.

For long seconds she kept herself rigid, hoping he would desist, but if anything, the movements grew more tantalising. 'Can't you stop!' she burst out at length, unable to endure the sexual tension any longer.

'You don't want me to stop.' His voice was mocking, yet unnervingly seductive.

'I do. . . .' she gasped hoarsely. 'Take me home.'

She saw his head descending. She watched it, mesmerised, unable to turn away. Inches away from her, he murmured, 'You want it, Sara.'

She made an attempt to wriggle away as his lips claimed hers. But it was only a half-hearted attempt, for she had not reckoned with the pent-up hunger exploding through her body. With a sigh she relaxed against him.

His mouth left hers and began to plant a trail of kisses over the rest of her face. There was a burning sensation in her ears, her eyes, her throat, as Clyde's lips moved over them. There was a teasing lightness in his lips, as if he remembered the arousal he could achieve with the excitement of his touch.

By the time his lips came back to hers the blood

was singing in her veins and she felt as if all her body was on fire. Willingly her lips opened to his, and she was swept by an anguished delight that left no room for thought. Convulsively she reached for him, her hands knotting themselves in the thick fair hair.

She shuddered as his mouth lifted again, then started a nerve-tingling descent along her throat once more, nudging aside the collar of her open-necked shirt. She closed her eyes as she felt his lips in the hollow between her breasts, following the swell first of one breast, then the other, pausing at last to capture a small nipple that had grown pink and hard with her desire.

And then he was pulling her across his lap, and she could feel his thighs hard and muscled against her, could sense that his depth of wanting was similar to her own. He was bending her backwards, one hand supporting the fragile weight of her neck, and she was yielding to him, helping him, the hands that had been in his hair now clasped on both sides of his head, pulling him to her.

Clyde drew away quite suddenly, and through a blur she stared up at him, at a loss to know why his mood had changed.

'Clyde. . . .' It was just a whisper.

'I want you. God, Sara, I want you!'

'Yes. . . .'

'But not here, in this car, like this. . . .'

The car! Reality came surging back in a rush as she felt the edge of the steering-wheel against her shoulder, and she wondered how she could have been so lost to all reason to have forgotten where they were.

'Someone might see us.' She struggled up.

'We'll go to your house.'

'No!' She threw the word at him blindly. 'I don't want it. . . .'

'Liar.' The blur had cleared and she could see his eyes. They were blue and clear, and she knew that he could see to the very core of her being. Still she had to try.

'What happened just now. . . .' She struggled for words. 'I didn't mean . . . didn't think. . . .' It was coming out badly. With an effort she faced him. 'I don't want it, Clyde.'

The corners of his mouth lifted. 'You *are* a liar.' He laughed softly, seductively, breath so close to her that she trembled. 'You do want me to make love to you. Your body says it all for you.' He paused, and the eyes that held hers were steady. 'In this one respect at least nothing has changed.'

CHAPTER EIGHT

RESTLESSLY Sara moved around the shop. Monday. A long week stretched ahead, and for that she was grateful. The holiday season was in full swing now and many tourists came to the Antique Den. Sara was busy constantly. When she returned to Morning Glow at night she was exhausted. It was an exhaustion she welcomed, for it gave her no time to think.

It was more than a week since she had seen Clyde last. The drive back to Morning Glow had been silent and strained. Sara had arranged her dishevelled clothing as best as she could, and had sat stiffly, staring out of her window, willing the miles away. Reaching the house, she had opened the door of the car, then looked back at Clyde. Green eyes had been wide and troubled, and the words that had tumbled on her lips were stilled before they could be uttered.

'There's nothing to say,' Clyde had said enigmatically, reading her thoughts. 'Goodbye, Sara.'

Wordlessly she had closed the door and had watched him drive away. A flame had been rekindled between them. It had seen its first sparks on the beach some weeks earlier, and had flared today almost to the point where it could not be controlled.

It was only when she reached her room that she remembered Andrea. What would be the reaction of Clyde's wife to what had happened? Or was she too sure of Clyde's love to care about an attraction which, on his part at least, was only physical? Had she been married to Clyde, Sara thought, she could not have been so forgiving. But Andrea's world was different from her own. Perhaps she herself indulged in an occasional affair, so that what her husband did in the backwoods was of little interest.

And what about Clyde himself? Didn't it worry him that he had been making love to his ex-fiancée when his wife was away from him? She would never have answers to her questions, Sara knew. Clyde's goodbye had had a ring of finality. For her own peace of mind, the sooner she put the whole episode out of her mind the better.

And that was easier said than done. It was impossible to focus her mind on anything else. There had been no word from Clyde on Sunday. Monday, with its return to work, had brought relief, but of a temporary kind only. Sara had found herself tense with waiting.

At each sound of the door-chimes she grew rigid, fearful that the customer who entered would be Clyde. A tall man seen at a distance was enough to make her heartbeat move quickly, subsiding only when the man turned out to be a stranger.

The week passed. The weekend came and went and still there was no word from him. She should be glad, she told herself—and wished that she was not so filled with numbness.

A shipment of porcelain had arrived, and Sara was unpacking it when the chimes sounded. The shop had been especially busy today. This time she did not turn. She had to get the porcelain stacked.

Customers would approach her when they had decided on their purchases.

A low voice, close to her ear, said, 'Hello, Sara.' Startled, she jerked up, and heard a vase break at her feet.

'Do I have such a shattering effect on you?' he asked teasingly.

More shattering than you could ever imagine, she thought. Aloud she said, 'My hand slipped. Did you want something, Clyde?'

'Not even a hello? Are you always so abrupt?'

'I'm busy,' she said shakily.

'I won't keep you a moment longer than necessary,' he countered smoothly, the teasing tone gone. 'Do you still have the Cape silver tea-service? I came in for that the first time.'

'In the corner. . . .' She gestured.

'Show it to me.'

'You can look at it by yourself.'

A lazy flicker of ice-blue eyes. 'I want you to show it to me. I take it you're something of an expert?'

He was baiting her, she knew, but she hoped she was equal to it. Lifting her head, she said, 'I'll be glad to tell you anything you want to know.'

She stood a little to one side as he examined the tea-service. It was very beautiful, attractively shaped and well looked after. Clyde gave it the respect it deserved. Sara watched him touching the tea-pot, running his hands carefully over the milk jug and the sugar-bowl, feeling for the delicate engraving on the tray, studying its identification marks. She could not take her eyes away from his hands, the fingers well-shaped and sensitive. Hands

which were as adept in arousing a woman to
ecstasy as they were in the art of healing.

Clyde had many questions, and Sara's manner
was calm and casual as she answered them, concealing the turmoil that raged inside her. Surely by
this time she should be able to remain indifferent
to him! But it was hard to remain indifferent to a
man who exuded strength and virility and a compelling sex appeal just as naturally as he breathed.
Almost unconsciously she found herself noting as
she always did every detail of his appearance: the
intelligent features, the shock of fair hair reaching
to the base of his neck, the muscular build which
could so easily have been that of an athlete; the
laughter lines beside his mouth. There was power
in every line of the long body, and a maleness to
which her senses had to respond.

He looked up unexpectedly, a smile in eyes that
were as blue as the shirt he wore. 'You really do
know something about antiques,' he observed.

For a moment she stared at him wordlessly. She
had not seen him smile at her quite like this since
she had ended their engagement. If only she could
just throw herself into his arms and tell him the
truth and to hell with the consequences! She took
a step towards him, only to check herself just in
time.

'You really are a chauvinist,' she said crossly.

'Don't you recognise a compliment?' He was still
smiling. 'Do *you* like the set, Sara?'

'I love it. It's one of the finest things in the
shop.'

'Hm. In that case I think I'll take it.' There was
an expression in his eyes which she could not

define. Just as she could not have explained why the blood flowed suddenly faster in her veins.

She was carrying the tea-service to the counter when he said, 'I have an invitation.'

'An invitation?' She was all at once breathless. And then, to cover her eagerness, 'You can tell me about it while I put this in a box.'

Carefully she began to wrap each piece in paper tissue. The awareness which had been with her since the moment Clyde had stepped into the shop had not left her. To conceal it she made her movements deliberately slow.

'If you have nothing planned, come to Cape Town with me on Saturday,' he said. 'I have tickets for something special.'

'Oh?' She looked up at him, and this time she could not hide her eagerness. She did not know that to the watching man her eyes were like sun-warmed sea. She was about to say yes, yes, of course I'll go, I just want to be with you, when something made her ask, 'Tickets for what, Clyde?'

'Ballet.' His voice could not have been more casual. 'A new production of *Romeo and Juliet*.'

She looked down quickly, concealing her eyes beneath long curling lashes. She went on wrapping the silver, but now, though her movements were even slower than before, she could not hide their trembling.

'Well, Sara, will you come?'

'No!'

A hand reached for her chin, cupping it, tilting it upward. Eyes in which the light had died were forced to meet his gaze.

'Why can't you come?' he asked grimly.

'Because I . . . I'd forgotten a date. There . . . there's this man in the village. He asked me ages ago. . . .'

'I couldn't ask you to break an arrangement,' he said so flatly that the double meaning was not lost on her. 'Tell me what I owe you for the silver, and we'll take a rain check on the ballet.'

'Let's do that,' Sara agreed, but as Clyde left the shop she knew that she would never accompany him. The new production of *Romeo and Juliet* was not unknown to her. Peter had been working on the choreography at the time of his death, and she knew that Madame Olga had considered it one of the best things he had done. It would not seem right to watch it with another man. But sentiment was not the only consideration that would keep her from going.

The pain of giving up dancing was with her still. Watching a ballet, particularly this one, would intensify the wounds. Much as the thought of going out with Clyde had excited her—and there was no denying to herself that she had been excited—she knew that seeing her old friends go through the motions which were now denied to her would be more than she could endure.

As before she wondered about Andrea. Clyde had said nothing about a threesome. A thought came to mind, not a new one. Andrea could be temporarily away from the city—a fact which would answer a few of Sara's questions about what seemed an unusual relationship. That being the case, it was possible that Andrea did not object to her husband escorting another girl, especially when she knew of his basic contempt for her.

The running of the shop was becoming routine. Never boring—it was impossible to be bored when she was surrounded by objects each with their own individual history and beauty, but routine all the same.

Now and then postcards arrived from Lynn, breezy, cheerful comments on the sights she was seeing. Her mother had all but recovered from her illness and was enjoying the trip with the same enthusiasm as her daughter. 'Bless you for helping me out,' Lynn would write. But she never added an address at which she could be reached. Perhaps it never occurred to her that her deputy might run into difficulties, Sara thought wryly. She could not know that Sara wanted to give up the running of the shop so that she could leave Morning Glow to find a place to live where she would never see Clyde.

She closed the shop earlier than usual one afternoon so that she could attend an auction of Cape Dutch furniture, but one look at the objects on display told her they were not right for the Antique Den. There was no point in staying.

It was still early as she made her way back along the coastal road. Turning a bend, she saw the white-walled beauty of Stellenberg against the forested mountain slope. She slowed the car.

She had thought of Jenny often of late. She had not been able to forget the little girl with the huge eyes in the tiny white face. Though she had had good reason for refusing to dance at the concert, the child's disappointment had nevertheless weighed on her mind. Sara hated to hurt people, and the knowledge that she had hurt a child as ill and as lovely as Jenny was not easy to live with.

For days she had toyed with the idea of visiting Jenny. All the children she had met at Stellenberg had drawn her compassion, but Jenny had touched a special part of her heart. She knew that only the dread of running into Clyde had kept her from going back long ago to see the little girl. Which was ridiculous, Sara had told herself firmly this morning; she could surely not be quite so weak-willed as to let Clyde inhibit her. She wanted to see Jenny, and she did not need Clyde's permission for that.

With this thought in mind she had packed a few books in a bag—ballet books with photographs of famous dancers and stories of the better-known classical ballets. She had known that she was going to the auction, and that there was every possibility that she might leave early, giving her a chance to visit the home before dark. If she did not manage to see Jenny today she would find another opportunity to do so.

As she took the turn-off that led to Stellenberg she could not help hoping that she would not see Clyde. Just the thought of him made her feel suddenly weak at the knees. She could no more stop loving him than she could stop breathing. But it was a love that had been doomed a long while ago, and for her own peace of mind the less she saw of him the better. That being the case, the visit would be more comfortable without him. At this time of day, she assured herself, he would be working. It was unlikely that she would see him.

Sara found Jenny where she had met her the first day, the wheelchair perched on a rise that overlooked the sea; yet not beneath the shade of the jacaranda this time, for it was not as warm as it had been earlier in the day. Jenny did not see Sara approach. An open book lay on her lap, but she was not reading. She was gazing across the dip of the lawn to the sea. The expression on a face that seemed even tinier than when Sara had seen it last was wistful. In Jenny's huge eyes was a look of knowledge and acceptance far beyond her years. Seeing it, Sara felt a stab of pain, and wished she had not taken so long to make this visit.

'Hello, Jenny,' she said as cheerfully as she could.

As recognition set in the near-adult sadness vanished and Jenny was a child once more. 'Mrs Burod!'

'How've you been, honey?'

'Okay.' The little girl looked around her. 'Dr Clyde didn't say you were coming.'

'He doesn't know I'm here.'

'Oh . . .?' The child was puzzled.

'I didn't come to see Dr Clyde. I came to see you.'

'Me?' The little face took on sudden radiance. 'Oh, Mrs Burod! I never have visitors.'

'Don't you have any family, Jenny?' asked Sara gently.

'Dad died when I was three, and Mom had an accident two years ago.'

'I'm so sorry,' Sara said gently, hiding a compassion that threatened to overwhelm her. 'I'd like to come more often, Jenny. Honey, I brought something for you.'

Dropping on to her knees beside the chair, she gave Jenny the bag, then watched as she took out the books. Cheeks that had been too white took on a flush of excitement as Jenny looked at the titles.

'Ballet stories!' Her voice was high with excitement. 'You remember!'

She began to turn the pages, pausing here and there to study a picture. Evidently she knew the names of all the well-known dancers, and had her own favourites amongst them. Sara sat quietly watching her.

At their first meeting she had been struck by the little girl's frailness, and that frailness seemed to have increased since then. The look of transparency had been heightened, and with it the air of weakness. Sick at heart, Sara wondered whether it was only in her imagination that Jenny appeared to have declined very rapidly.

Clyde had told her the child might not have long to live; he had gone into some detail. Sara wondered if Jenny knew the extent of her illness. Remembering the sad acceptance in the big eyes she understood that she did.

'Mrs Burod, what super books!' For the moment Jenny was like any other ten-year-old, enthralled with a new present.

Sara forced a smile. 'Shall we look at them together?'

Soon they were absorbed in a discussion about *Coppélia*. It was a ballet Jenny knew only vaguely, and she listened entranced as Sara told her the story of the clockwork doll made by an old toymaker. She was even more entranced when she heard how the ballet was danced, how the ballerina, pretending to be the doll come to life, would first portray her with stiff clockwork movements, her dancing only becoming more fluid as the story progressed.

'Something like this,' Sara said, moving her head and her arms in short wooden movements.

'I love that!' Jenny's laughter rang out, high and joyous. 'Oh, I'm so glad you came, Mrs Burod.'

'So am I,' a voice said from behind them.

'Dr Clyde!' Jenny exclaimed as Sara jerked upwards to stare into the blue eyes of the man towering above her.

'Mrs Burod brought me these super books,' Jenny said happily, oblivious of the tension suddenly filling the air. 'It was such a surprise.'

'A surprise indeed,' Clyde agreed, then added, 'But a nice one.'

Absurdly Sara was swept with a sudden rush of pleasure. His words were more than just a statement made for Jenny's benefit. The look in his eyes told her that he was genuinely glad that she had come. Glad that she had come to give Jenny some happiness, not because he himself felt any joy at seeing her, she told herself a moment later. And yet the lovely feeling remained with her.

'Mrs Burod was telling me the story of *Coppélia*. She was doing the doll dance,' Jenny chattered on.

'So I saw,' came the quiet comment.

Sara's cheeks were suffused with sudden warmth. Had Clyde been watching long? she wondered. She rose to her feet in a lithe movement and put a hand through her windswept hair. Glancing at her watch, she saw that she had been here longer than she had imagined. The patch of sun had been infiltrated by the shadows of a late afternoon.

'Time for Jenny to be going inside,' said Clyde, as if guessing her thoughts. 'I see one of the staff coming to fetch her.'

'Mrs Burod. . . .' The little girl's voice was hesitant. 'Won't you change your mind about dancing at the concert?'

She should have been prepared, of course, but oddly she wasn't. They were both watching her—Clyde, his eyes narrowed and intent, Jenny almost pathetically eager. Fingers digging into the palms of her hands, Sara said, 'No, Jenny.'

'You'll come to see me again soon?'

'Of course I will. Very soon.' She bent to drop a kiss on a cheek that felt dry and a little too cool. 'Goodbye, honey.' And then, turning to the man who had been silent throughout the interchange, 'Goodbye, Clyde.'

'I'll walk with you to your car,' he said.

No doubt he meant to question her once more about what he saw as her stubbornness. After seeing Jenny's decline she would find it even harder than the last time to convince him that she did not want to dance. And yet, even while she braced herself to meet his scathing remarks, Sara's senses leaped at his closeness.

Last time she had seen him had been in the Antique Den, he had been dressed in casual clothes. Now, in the white safari suit he wore for work, he looked just as attractive. His arms and throat emerged long and tanned and muscled from the short-sleeved open-collared jacket. His eyes held a distant brooding look, so that she wondered what he was thinking. His stride, though it was slowed to match hers, was lithe and easy. He had been working all day, Sara knew, and yet there was nothing tired in his face. He looked as fresh as if he had just returned from a swim in the surf.

He spoke into the silence. 'Jenny likes you.'

Now it would come, the challenge to dance. Quietly she said, 'I like her too.'

'It was nice of you to come today.'

'I've been wanting to see her again.'

'She'll enjoy the books.'

The conversation was taking a different slant from the one she had expected. 'I hope so,' Sara said. And then, 'You didn't mind me coming here today, Clyde, without letting you know first?'

'Of course not. I only had to look at Jenny's face to see what the visit meant to her. Come whenever you can.'

She wanted to talk about Jenny, to ask more about the little girl's illness, when Clyde said, 'I intended to claim some of your time too.'

She looked up at him. 'Oh?'

'I'm driving in to Cape Town at the weekend, and I want you to come with me. We'll be joining up with another couple for the evening.' He grinned down at her. 'Bring a pretty dress.'

Statements, not questions. As if Clyde took it for granted that people would automatically fall in with his wishes. She should be off-putting, Sara knew, but found it impossible. Just the thought of spending a day with Clyde sent the blood singing in her veins. Through an excitement which drove out all but the most pressing questions she asked,

'What about Andrea?'

'Stop worrying about Andrea. I'll pick you up just after nine.'

Sara's mind was a whirl as she drove back to Morning Glow. Clyde's unexpected invitation had filled her with joy. She had given up telling herself that she did not love him, or that the loving was a condition she would grow out of. She would always love Clyde. Once she had married a man while loving another, and the marriage had been a success only because Peter Burod had been an exceptional man, but it was unlikely that she would marry again. It was just as unlikely that the paths of her life and Clyde's could converge indefinitely. That being the case, she might as well make the most of their infrequent times together.

The thought of Andrea did not trouble her as much as it had done at the start. She knew by now that the Montgomerys' marriage was unusual. Andrea, it seemed, was a woman who led her own life, even if that meant long stretches away from her husband. If Clyde minded the separation he was able to conceal it.

There was of course the matter that Clyde should not be going out with another woman. But he seemed to see nothing wrong with it, and he had intimated that Andrea felt the same way. Sara knew that if she was in Andrea's position she would want to scratch out the eyes of any woman who went out with her husband. But then if she was in Andrea's position she would not spend more time away from her husband than she could possibly help. Impatiently she shook her head; she could not have reached the age of twenty-four without knowing that one could not judge another person's values by one's own.

What mattered was that she would be spending a day with Clyde, one whole day to add to her reservoir of memories. She had refused his last invitation because she did not want to see ballet, but this invitation was another matter, and Sara meant to enjoy the day to the fullest.

Her thoughts turned to Jenny, and now she was troubled. Her intention to ask Clyde about the child had been forgotten with the unexpectedness of his invitation. Jenny's joy at the visit had been as warming as her increased weakness had been disturbing. Sara knew that she must go to see the little girl as often as possible.

Clyde fetched her early. The first light of dawn was just creeping over the horizon when they left Morning Glow.

'Brought everything you need?' he had asked, as he had put her overnight bag in the boot of the car.

'I certainly hope so.' She had smiled up at him. 'If there's something I've forgotten I can always get it in Cape Town.'

An early morning chill was in the air, a damp coldness that was inside the car as well as outside. It took a while for Sara to register it, for her excitement had dulled her feelings to anything else. They were some miles from Morning Glow when she realised that she had forgotten to bring a thick sweater. In her case in the boot of the car was an evening shawl, a lovely thing of silver and white thread, but that delicate garment was hardly appropriate now. She shivered.

'Feeling cold?' Clyde asked.

'A little.'

'A lot,' he corrected her cheerfully. 'Your teeth are rattling. Didn't you bring a sweater?'

'I forgot,' she acknowledged ruefully.

'There's one way of keeping warm.'

She looked at him with relief. 'You have a car-heater?'

'I do, but it will make the air stuffy.' He turned and grinned at her, white teeth glinting wickedly in the tanned face. 'We both know a better way to keep warm.'

Her heart skittered inside her. 'I'll be fine.'

'For one small girl you are surprisingly stubborn.' His voice was lazy, so that Sara was unprepared for the hand that left the wheel and scooped her to him.

She lay against him a moment, the virile smell of him filling her nostrils and dizzying her mind. Then she struggled up. It took surprising effort to make herself rigid, even more effort to infuse her limbs with the strength they needed to move away from him.

The arm around her shoulders tightened, defying her to move. 'Relax, little one,' Clyde commanded.

'I t-told you, I'll be fine.'

'You'd sound more convincing if you weren't so breathless.' She heard him laugh, the sound soft, seductive, and the shiver that went through her body had nothing to do with the cold.

'We . . . we'll have an accident,' she said jerkily.

'We've never had one before.' How could a man's voice be light and amused and yet tantalisingly provocative all at the same time? Sara wondered.

There was a point at which it became too difficult to fight him. Perhaps because to do so she had first to win an impossible victory over herself. With a shudder she relaxed against him, her head resting just below the hard ridge of his shoulder.

'Good, isn't it?' Clyde asked softly.

'Very good,' she agreed, and knew that neither of them were discussing the efficiency of shared bodily warmth.

Savour these moments, Sara told herself as she rested against him. Enjoy this harmony, for there was no knowing when she would experience anything quite like it again.

She made no effort at small talk and was glad that Clyde was silent too. All thought of pulling herself away from him, to sit in dignified and shivering isolation at her end of the seat, had fled. If anything, she wished only that this drive could go on and on.

Against her cheek was Clyde's sweater, rough and warm. She could feel the rippled muscles of his chest and arm, and against her soft thigh the hardness of his. Every one of her senses was alert to him, aware and excited. Even now, when he was concentrating on the driving, there emanated from him an aura of sensuousness and virility which was overpowering. To his patients his professional aspect might appear dominant; to Sara, it was his maleness which made the greater impact, a basic animal-like quality to which every core of her femininity had to respond.

The forests were dark and brooding, and

through Clyde's half-opened window the air was fresh and sweet. The mountains were great dark shapes silhouetted against the lightening sky. Mist hung over the sea and if there were any ships on the water they could not be seen.

Later, when the sun was high in the sky and colours were vivid, traffic would be heavy. So spectacular was the loveliness of the Garden Route that tourists in their thousands came to pay homage. But this early morning mystery had its own beauty.

Usually Sara was enchanted with the sight of brooding lagoons and lonely beaches, of rugged headlands where in centuries past many a ship had come to grief, and of forests where the trees were so thick and tall that no light entered. This morning her mind, her senses, were centred only on the man who stirred her beyond anything she had ever known.

His throat rose above the line of the sweater. Sara could feel the strong thrust of it from where she lay. A longing swept her to feel the bare skin. She pulled herself up an inch or two, then let her lips rest unashamedly against the rough pulsating flesh. Still Clyde said nothing, but the beat of his heart had increased. It gave Sara joy to know that he was not entirely indifferent to her.

A little later he spoke into the silence. 'Hungry?'

'No,' Sara said.

'I am.' There was nothing remotely romantic in his tone. 'You'll find a bag of food under my seat.'

Sara bent forward. As she reached towards the paper bag her arm made contact with one long leg. The calf was flexed and hard. The breath jerked in her lungs, so that for a moment she could not move. Then she lifted the bag and sat upright. As she turned to face Clyde she knew that her cheeks were flushed.

'Help yourself,' she said, holding the open bag toward him.

'I don't have a spare hand.' The arm which had returned to her shoulder increased its pressure, as if to reinforce the fact.

'No. . . .' The lovely closeness had meant nothing to him then, she thought dully.

'Where are you going?' he asked, as she made to move away.

'I'm giving you back your hand. You can't eat like this.'

'Can't I?' His tone was lazy, tantalising.

'How will you manage?'

A low husky laugh, then Clyde said, 'For a girl who can snuggle up to a man as you did just now you show amazingly little imagination.' Turning his eyes from the road, he subjected her to a long amused stared that missed nothing of her appearance, noting cheeks which had grown even redder and lips that trembled just slightly and eyes that were big and wide and luminous.

'You have *your* hands,' he said very softly.

His meaning was clear; she did not need to have it put into words. Despite the trembling inside her she managed to meet his lazy amusement with a glance almost as steady as his own. Well, and why not! she thought. Giving what she hoped was a nonchalant shrug, she opened the paper bag, took out a sandwich and held it near to his mouth.

'Which is it?' he wanted to know. 'Chicken or egg?'

Two could play at this game. 'Taste,' she said.

Clyde laughed appreciatively. Then she saw his tongue approach the bread, felt it curl around the fingers that held it, the feel of it sensuous and slow. Flame licked her fingers, her hand, shot towards her spine and along it. Only with an effort of will did she maintain a steady hand and a calm exterior.

'Good,' he said, and once more she knew he was referring to something other than the obvious.

'Sure you can manage?' She wondered later how she was able to keep her voice so cool.

'As long as you can.'

He saw through her effort to appear composed, knew the effect he was having on her. Damn him, she thought, he had always known how she felt, always would. Only one set of facts was secret from him, and that would always remain secret.

He bit into the bread and his teeth grazed the side of her fingers. Sara could have sworn he did it deliberately, but the knowledge did nothing to stop a torrent of desire from flooding her system. It hit her unexpectedly and hard, so that she was overcome with the desire to go into his arms.

'How is the silver tea-set?' she asked, for something to say.

'Just fine.' A hint of amusement, indicating that he knew her need to make small-talk.

'You've used it?' she asked with grim determination.

Another bite. She felt the strong teeth nibble, just for a moment, at the soft inner part of one finger.

'I'm waiting for the right occasion,' he answered, when he had swallowed. 'Don't take that away, Sara. I haven't had breakfast.'

She held the bread to his mouth and felt the curl of his tongue against her palm as he took another bite. At the same time the hand on her shoulder flattened, curved. She could feel every one of his long fingers through the thin fabric of her blouse.

'You must keep it polished,' she said shakily.

'Regularly,' he promised her solemnly. 'Mm, this chicken is good. You really should try some.'

She jerked around. 'Haven't you damn well had enough yourself?'

'I've just begun,' he said lazily, and she saw his eyes gleam.

He finished the sandwich and asked for another. Without acknowledging his game—something she was oddly loath to do—Sara had little choice but to give in to him. All her body was on fire as she fed him. The contact with lips and tongue continued, the movements sensual and outrageous— and outwardly innocent, as if any contact was purely coincidental.

Sara drew out the conversation for as long as she could. 'Did you know that a Cape governor once owned that set?' she asked, as Clyde's tongue once more touched her hand.

'Mm-hm. I imagine you told me.'

'It's really very valuable. Ouch!' She drew back enraged as one finger was caught between his teeth and nipped. 'Why did you do that?'

'To stop you acting like a prim miss.'

'I . . . I'm not acting,' she said weakly. 'I . . . I thought you were interested in your purchase.'

'You want me,' he said quietly.

She dropped her hand, letting the sandwich fall. 'Do you always have to be so direct?'

'And I want you.'

'Clyde, don't. . . .' She stopped, tears pricking at her eyes, not knowing how to go on, not even knowing what she wanted to say.

'Don't what?' he asked very quietly. 'Don't say what's in both our minds? That we want to make love?'

She shook her head violently. 'No. . . .'

'Yes, Sara. You've changed, I've changed. But that hasn't changed, that spark that was always between us.' And then, fiercely, as she shook her head again, 'You know damn well that's the truth.'

'Yes. . . .' She had not known she would agree until the word emerged.

The car jerked, then drew smoothly to a halt at a viewpoint a few yards farther on. At this time of the day there were no cars parked on the sandy verge.

Sara did not resist him as he twisted in his seat and put his other arm around her. She did not turn away as his head descended and his mouth came down on hers. There was a hunger inside her that had been with her a long time, and for once she made no outward pretence of denying it.

His kiss was as brief as it was passionate. 'Damn!' Clyde swore as he lifted his head. 'Wheel's in the way. Move over, Sara.'

He did not release his hold on her as she shifted in her seat, but moved with her. They turned to face each other simultaneously, coming together in the manner of two people drawn by a common need. His mouth did not go directly to hers, but found the different features of her face instead — her eyes, the curve of a cheek, the lobe of an ear and the skin beneath it. His lips played on her lightly, tantalisingly, exploring and tasting with a sensuous life of their own. Sara put her hands on either side of his head, feeling the chiselled contours beneath her palms, the springy hair between her fingers. Unlike all the other times, there was no sense of holding back, of maintaining a pretence. There was only the wonderful joyousness of holding him.

His lips left her face and went to her throat, planting tiny kisses along a column that had never seemed more sensitive, lingering a moment in the hollow where the pulse beat too fast, then ascending once more. When his mouth came down on hers at last she was ready for him, her lips opening willingly beneath his.

There was no lightness now in his kiss, just a passionate thirst that could not be slaked. As his lips began an exploration of the sweetness of her mouth, his hands went beneath her blouse, pushing it upwards, moving over the bare skin. One hand slid down over her hips, the other curved forward to cup a small firm breast in its palm.

As he caught the nipple between his fingers, stroking it, letting it grow hard, Sara gave a small cry. The pleasure he stirred in her was exquisite; it was also so intense as to bring pain. She was only just hanging on to the barest vestige of control, enough to know that if they did not pull apart now they would not be able to do so later.

'Someone will see us,' she managed to whisper when Clyde lifted his mouth to draw breath.

'Right.' His voice was husky with emotion. 'It wouldn't do for us to be caught on the highway making love. Not the first time we've had to stop for that reason!'

He was behind the wheel once more, starting the ignition, when he said, 'We would have made love. All the way. Had we not been in the car there'd have been no stopping. You know that, Sara, don't you?'

She knew it. She knew that she could not have stopped him, because she would first have had to find a way of stopping herself. She was on her own side of the seat now, a small figure, bereft at the sudden isolation despite the fact that she had been the one to suggest it.

'Next time we won't stop,' Clyde said very definitely. 'You know that too.'

The car was fleet and smooth. A mile had been covered when Sara spoke again. 'What about Andrea?' she asked in a low tone. 'What would Andrea have said?'

'Forget about Andrea.' There was a strange inflection in Clyde's voice. 'Just for today, please forget about Andrea.'

CHAPTER NINE

SHE had not thought about Andrea once, Sara realised as she dressed for the evening. The day had been so perfect that there had been no time to brood.

Clyde had been the old Clyde she had once known—devastatingly handsome and compelling male as always, intelligent and devil-may-care, but also fun to be with. As for herself—when they had walked through the streets of Cape Town, shopping as they could not do in the village, and then later, sunbathing on the beach, Sara had found it hard to believe that quite so much had happened in her life since the days when she had been a busy dancer engaged to be married to the man who had taken her emotions by storm.

Clyde had reserved two rooms at a modern shore-front hotel in Sea Point. His room adjoined hers, and Sara wondered if he had planned it that way. In her present euphoric state of mind she would not have minded if he had.

Bring something pretty, he had said, when he had first mentioned the trip. Looking at herself in the mirror, Sara was satisfied that her choice had been a good one. The Grecian-styled dress of deep jade did wonderful things for her. Her hair looked darker, glossier, her colouring was more vivid. Her figure in the soft folds of the dress was at once delicate and intensely feminine.

In the next room Clyde would be changing from

the casual clothes he had worn during the day. Sara could imagine him pulling a silk shirt over the bronzed body, running a comb through hair that felt vital and springy to the touch. Just the thought of him dressing only yards distant from her was enough to intensify the sense of anticipation which had been with her all day. She had not realised until this moment quite how much she had been looking forward to this evening.

At a knock she opened the door and Clyde stepped into the room. He looked very tall in a well-cut grey suit, distinguished and as devilishly attractive as she had expected. His eyes darkened as he took in her own appearance, and then as their eyes met, and he reached for her hands, she felt the adrenalin pumping through her system.

'You're beautiful.' Simple words, but his voice was husky.

In another moment she would be in his arms. Already she felt the treacherous longing sweep her. She remembered what he had said in the car; next time there would be no stopping. The weakness in her legs, the pounding of her heart in her chest, told her that if he touched her now she would be powerless even to ask him to stop.

'Your friends,' she said unsteadily, as he drew her to him.

'You have an incredible sense of timing.' His tone had become mocking. 'But for once you happen to be right. My friends will be waiting.'

They had dinner in a small sophisticated restaurant on the sea-front. As Sara and Clyde walked to their table, many eyes turned their way. The interested glances were for them both, as a couple,

Sara knew, and felt a pang of unhappiness at the knowledge that the image they presented was sham, a relationship that could not last beyond this one stolen weekend in time.

Clyde's friends joined them minutes later, and Sara liked them on sight. Their names were Graham and Ann. Newly-married, they were both doctors not long in the city. It was soon evident that they did not know that Sara had ever had any importance in Clyde's life, and for that she was grateful. If they knew Andrea, and wondered at Clyde's appearance with another woman, they made no comment.

The conversation was lively, the dinner delicious. Sara was almost sorry when Clyde glanced at his watch before calling for the bill. She had not been so stimulated for a long time.

It was only as they were entering the Theatre that it occurred to her that she did not know the nature of what they were to see.

'*A Midsummer Night's Dream*,' Clyde matter-of-factly answered her question.

'The play?' she asked, through parched lips.

'The ballet.'

'No!' She stared at him. Her expression was one of horror. There were people behind her, crowds making their way towards the auditorium, pushing past her. She did not notice them.

'No!' she said again.

'Come along, Sara.' It was a command, though strangely there was no harshness in his tone.

Shaking her head, she pivoted blindly, oblivious of the crowds, of Clyde's friends. There was only one thought: she had to get away.

Fingers gripped her arm just above the elbow—outwardly a friendly gesture, one that would not cause any bystander to comment, but Sara felt steel in the touch, the unyielding will.

She looked up at him again. 'I can't! Clyde, please. . . .'

Through the blur of tears she did not register the watchfulness in eyes that were now dark as a twilight sky.

'Come along, Sara,' he ordered again. With his firmness there was surprising gentleness, as if he sensed her distress and felt in some way sorry for it. And then, as she was about to protest further, he said so softly that only she could hear him, 'Graham and Ann are just behind us. They'll be wondering. . . . We'll talk afterwards.'

Perhaps she could have stood her ground. Later she would wonder what would have happened if she had done so. But in those moments in the thronging auditorium it was as if all freedom of choice had deserted her, so that she had no alternative but to let the hand on her arm and the momentum of the crowds propel her along.

They were shown to their seats. Sara sat between Clyde and Ann. A buzz of anticipation filled the air. It was strange to be experiencing the pre-performance excitement from the front of the curtain rather than from behind; despite her agitation Sara registered that fact.

To the left of her, Clyde was quiet. Sara did not notice that it was a grim kind of quietness. To the right of her Ann was leafing through her programme.

'I've heard this is a fantastic production,' she said.

'I've heard that too.' Somehow Sara managed to say the words.

No mention of Peter Burod; perhaps in the medical world of Ann and Graham his name had no meaning. It was evident that Ann had not made the connection between Sara's name and that of the choreographer. It was evident also that Clyde's friends did not know that she had once been a ballet dancer.

Ann was still talking, but the words washed over Sara. There was only one thought in her mind: Clyde had trapped her—knowingly, deliberately. For reasons of his own he had led her into a situation from which she could not escape.

She glanced at him. The dim light of the auditorium showed a profile that was stern and strong. Hawk-like, Sara thought, and shivered. The moments in the car earlier that day, when she had fed him sandwiches and felt the sensuous touch and nibble of lips and tongue, seemed more than just hours ago. Nothing sensuous about him now, just a sense of waiting, of grimness. The hawk delighting in its victim's helplessness.

The lights darkened, and the first bars of the overture sounded through the auditorium. Then the curtain rose on the first act of Peter Burod's *A Midsummer Night's Dream.*

Sara felt tension building inside her as the ballet began. Any ballet, she knew, would cause her pain. But this particular ballet, one in which she had danced herself, created a special anguish. Memories welled inside her, flooding her. Rehearsals, with Madame Olga controlling the dancers like puppets. Peter, always in the background, ready to advise with an interpretation or an explanation.

Clyde, coming backstage, wanting to meet the dancer who had caught his eye and his fancy. The beginnings of a courtship that had flamed into a love she had not anticipated.

Clyde had known that the evening would bring pain. He had chosen this ballet carefully—for what purpose he alone knew. But even Clyde could not guess quite the extent of Sara's pain. For he did not seem to know that she could never dance again, and therefore could not understand her torment at watching her former colleagues go through the motions that she would never perform again.

A lump had formed in her throat, hard and painful. Tears had gathered behind her eyelids, and she tried to keep them under control. She would *not* give Clyde the satisfaction of seeing her cry. But the tears began to spill nevertheless.

And then to her horror she began to weep. It was a weeping she could not control. A quiet weeping; not a sound escaped her, but the small body was rocked in spasms which she could not suppress.

She felt Clyde reach for one of her hands. She did not stop to wonder whether he offered comfort at a reaction that went beyond anything he had imagined. Abruptly she pulled her hand away.

Neither had her emotion escaped Ann. 'Sara . . . Sara, are you all right?' the girl at her side whispered.

Through her tears she tried to nod. She took a jerky breath. Somehow she must regain control. But the weeping grew stronger.

'Sara. . . .' Ann whispered again, her tone full of concern.

Sara could not answer. Nor could she sit here a moment longer. All her movements jerky now, she got to her feet, pushed past Ann and Graham, and hurried up the dark aisle.

She collapsed on a bench in the foyer. And now her weeping was no longer as silent as it had been. Great sobs racked her body.

'Sara!' Clyde's voice, urgent, concerned. Clyde's arms folded around her. 'Sara darling, what is it?'

She heard the endearment, but it made no impact on her frenzied mind. She tried to twist away from him, pushing her fists against his chest.

'Let me go!' she sobbed. 'Take me back to the hotel.'

He hesitated just a moment. 'All right.' His tone was strangely subdued. 'I'll just go back inside and tell the others we're going. Wait for me, Sara.'

Wait for me. . . . The words made an impact where the endearment had not. Wait for me—an order. Did Clyde think he could manipulate every facet of her life?

It would be a few minutes before he returned to the foyer. Enough time to let her make her own getaway.

Out of the building, and half a block up to the taxi rank where a vehicle was standing. A minute after Clyde had left her, Sara was on her way back to the hotel.

She was in her room and the door was locked when he knocked. She lay on the bed and looked at the door. Her weeping had stopped and now she felt numb, drained.

Clyde knocked again, then again. Then he called, 'Sara, let me in!'

She lay silent.

'Open the door! Immediately!' And then, when she did not answer, 'Sara! I know you're in there. Open up!'

'Go away,' she called, after a moment.

'Open the door!'

'I don't want to see you.'

'You will open up.' Even through the barrier of the door she could hear the threat in his tone. 'If you don't, I'll get in anyway.'

He would do just that, she knew, as she got off the bed. Clyde would always do what he wanted, get what he wanted. Strangely, people would want to give him his way. She had seen the force of his magnetism during their courtship, had experienced it again later. People would always be drawn to Clyde Montgomery—men, women; especially women.

But now was not the moment to contemplate the mystery of his charisma. More than ever she must be on her guard, must think clearly.

She opened the door just a crack. 'I don't want to see you.'

'I know.' Easily he stepped past her. 'We have to talk all the same.'

Sara stared up at him. Did he have no shame at all? No feelings of remorse? He stood very close to her, tall and lithe and muscular, compellingly masculine. She took a careful step backwards.

'We have nothing to say,' she said quietly. 'Leave me, Clyde.'

'What's the matter, Sara?'

'You know damn well!' she flared at him. 'You led me into a trap!'

'Only to get you to break out of the shell you've built around yourself.'

'So you admit you tricked me!'

'I admit I wasn't honest with you.' He reached for her hands. She tried to pull them away, but he folded them in his, palm against palm, his fingers curling round to her wrist. 'Come and sit down, Sara.'

'No,' she said firmly, and wondered despairingly why even now, when she was at her angriest, her pulses should be racing at the sensuousness of his touch. 'Just tell me why you tricked me.'

'It seemed the right thing. Perhaps I was wrong. . . .'

His eyes were very dark in the lamplight, their expression bleak. His skin seemed stretched tautly over his cheekbones and beneath his tan there was a hint of pallor. It came to Sara that she had shocked him, that for the first time she had caused Clyde to feel uncertain, and she knew a moment of satisfaction.

'You *were* wrong,' she said flatly.

'Come and sit with me,' he said again. 'Then we'll talk.'

She pushed against the coaxing hands. For a few moments she thought her persistence had won over his demands. When he lifted her against him, her surprise was so great that she lay still for a moment, her breathing erratic. By the time she had regained her sense of outrage he had put her down on the bed.

'I want to help you,' he said, before she could speak. 'You've erected a wall, Sara. Morning Glow is only the physical part of it. There's a mental one too. It's that one I wanted to tear down.'

'By taking me to a ballet that I didn't want to
see,' she said bitterly. 'You're a doctor, Clyde,
you're not a psychiatrist.'

'Psychiatry had no part in what I tried to do
tonight.' A hand cupped her chin, drawing up her
face, forcing her to look at him. 'I was acting
simply as a man who was once engaged to you,
who thought he understood you.'

If he had used the word 'love' she would have
broken down and told him everything, Sara knew.

'You don't understand me now,' she said, her
voice shaky.

Clyde's thumb left her chin and began a slow
stroking movement, up towards the lobe of one
ear, then down, along the sensitive column of a
slim throat, sending shivers coursing down her
spine.

'Some parts of you I understand,' he said softly,
so close to her that the warmth of his breath fanned
her cheek. 'Your senses give you away every time.'

'You do excite me,' Sara acknowledged steadily,
her eyes meeting his. 'You know that. But that's
where our level of communication ends.'

'I refuse to believe that.' Still the same movement, tantalising in its slowness. 'You can't go on
like this, Sara.'

'I'm perfectly happy.'

'No, darling, you're not.'

Darling! It came to her that he had used the
word earlier. Joy leaped suddenly inside her.
Perhaps after all she could tell Clyde all that she
had kept bottled up inside her for so long.

And then she remembered Andrea, and knew

that any love Clyde had felt for Sara herself no longer existed. 'Darling' was an endearment used loosely by many people; Clyde must be one of them.

'I am happy,' she insisted dully. 'I ... I'm not the girl you once knew, Clyde. My values have changed, the things I like. . . . But I am happy.'

The hand moved lower. It began to trail a path towards the cleavage of the dress, the fingers inserting themselves into the hollow between her breasts; caressing, teasing. It became harder and harder to maintain an expressionless interior when inside her she felt an agonising desire.

'If what you say is true,' said Clyde, never ceasing his movement, 'then you'd have agreed to come to the ballet with me the first time I asked you. And you wouldn't have been so affected tonight.'

'I don't want to talk about it any more.' Restlessly she tried to turn away from him. And found that she could not. There was a sinuous magic in Clyde's hand that held her captive more surely than a grip of iron could have done.

'You *must* talk.' His voice was more gentle than she had heard it. 'Sara, you can't continue to isolate yourself from the world. There must be a reason why you don't want to dance. You must talk to people. To me. . . .'

She had to end this conversation, quickly, before his spell could bring about her undoing. She closed her eyes against the handsomeness so close to her. It was harder to shut off her awareness of a maleness that dizzied her. But when she spoke her voice was surprisingly firm.

'I do talk to people. Other people. Not you,

Clyde.' She took a breath. 'Don't you know that I hate you?'

Silence. The stroking fingers ceased their movement, and abruptly the hands lifted away from her. Sara opened her eyes just a slit. He was watching her. His jaw was tight, his lips set.

As he met her gaze his face relaxed and the corners of his mouth tilted in a smile that was without humour. 'Seems there's no point in going on. I'll see you in the morning.'

He was at the door when she called him back. 'I want to go home tonight.'

'It's very late, Sara. And dark.'

'The road is good,' she said stubbornly. She shot him a challenging look. 'Don't you understand that I can't stand the thought of spending the night next door to you?'

If she had thought to discomfit Clyde, she had misjudged him. The gaze she was subjected to was insolent in the extreme, going from her face to her body, lingering on the crumpled gown, on the long legs that were bare where her dress had lifted.

'I think you'd rather spend it with me.' His eyes gleamed mockingly, the lips parting in a rakish grin. 'It just so happens that I've lost the taste for it. Get packed, Sara. We leave in twenty minutes.'

Sara took the road to Stellenberg on a day when she knew that there was no risk of meeting Clyde. She had learned that he spent Tuesday afternoons consulting at a children's clinic in a village twenty miles down the coast. By the time he got back to the home, she would already have left.

Jenny was not in her usual place beneath the

tree. As Sara made her way towards the white-walled building she felt a quiver of dread.

'Jenny has taken a bad turn,' she was informed by the nurse at the desk.

'Can't I see her? I won't stay long.'

'No, Mrs Burod. Dr Montgomery has ordered a ban on visitors.'

'Is she . . . is she very ill?'

'I'm afraid she is,' came the grave response.

Early next morning, after a night spent almost entirely sleepless, Sara phoned Stellenberg and asked for Clyde. 'How bad is Jenny?' she asked abruptly, coming straight to the point. It was the first time she had talked to him since the midnight drive back from Cape Town.

'Pretty bad,' he said quietly.

'Will she be at the concert?'

'I'm not sure. . . .'

'See that she's well enough to go.' Sara gripped the phone tightly. 'If she's there, I'll dance.'

'Sara!' An urgency in his tone. 'You're sure?'

'Quite sure.'

'What made you change your mind?'

'I'd like to give Jenny some happiness.'

And after all the hours of turmoil and sleeplessness it had been as simple as that, Sara thought, as she put down the phone. Jenny had touched her heart. Besides the fact that the child could be dying nothing else mattered. Not even the knowledge that by dancing Sara's own health could be harmed. What was all-important was that Jenny should experience the one joy she desired above all else.

Probably her health would not be affected, Sara reflected, as she walked along the beach in the late afternoon. Her collapse had happened a long time ago. She had been pregnant at the time, her body strained by rehearsals. She had been in good health ever since.

She chose a dance that would not be too demanding, and began to practise that night. At first she was dismayed by her stiffness; limbs that once had performed in response to a kind of conditioned instinct had become clumsy.

In ten days was the concert. She had enough time to prepare. Each day she practised. As the stiff limbs loosened, she felt an exhilaration that had been missing a long time. Dancing was part of her, part of the very fabric of her being, and until now she had not let herself realise quite how much she had missed it. While she was saddened by Jenny's illness, and while Clyde and a love which refused to fade were never far from her mind, Sara nevertheless experienced a satisfaction which belonged only to her dancing.

The day before the concert there was a call from Clyde. It was short and to the point. Jenny was a little better, she would be in the audience. Sara waited tensely, hoping for some personal words just for herself, but there were none. Clearly, after the débâcle of the night in Cape Town, what interest Clyde had still had in her was now gone.

She tried to push him from her mind as she decided on a costume. Something dainty, a costume that would bring to life the ballerinas Jenny had seen in pictures. Yet as she looked at herself in the mirror it was hard not to think of Clyde. She had worn a similar costume the first time he had seen her, when he had come to her dressing-room and begun to sweep her off her feet. Would the dress bring back memories? she wondered. Would it remind him of the love they had once shared?

But she would never know what Clyde felt. For one thing, he would not tell her. For another, she would not be here to listen even if he did.

Along with the decision to dance in the concert, Sara had made up her mind on something else. She was cutting Clyde out of her life. All along she had hoped that her love for him would fade, but if anything it had grown stronger. But it was a love without a future. Sara's chances of living a normal happy life—something she wanted quite desperately to do—depended on her distancing herself from the man she loved.

It could be only a matter of time before Andrea rejoined him at Stellenberg, and Sara did not want to be around when she did. Even without Andrea's presence, she knew that she could no longer lay herself open to the possibility of chance meetings. Her nerves were too raw, her emotions too vulnerable.

She was totally unable to stop her senses leaping whenever she saw Clyde. She was unable to quell the agonising longing to be in his arms, the wild desire to have him make love to her. She would always love him. She had known for some time that it was hopeless to expect otherwise. But for her own peace of mind she had to love him from afar.

Lynn's letter had arrived three days ago. Her mother was better, the cruise was almost at an end, and she was on her way back. She longed to see her Antique Den again, Lynn had written, and hoped that Sara might be willing to entertain the idea of a partnership.

Had circumstances been different Sara knew that she would have done just that. As it was, she would find something elsewhere. After the concert she would tell Clyde of her decision to leave Morning Glow on Lynn's return. She wondered if the news would interest him even slightly.

Clyde came to Morning Glow to take Sara to the concert. She had said she would drive her own car, but he insisted. Sara asked him about Jenny.

Clyde's tone was quiet as he talked, his face grave. Once, when he took his eyes from the road to look at her, Sara saw that they were warm with concern.

This was how she must remember him, she thought—the man of contrasts, strong and intoxicatingly masculine, and yet kind and dedicated and concerned at the same time. The tight navy cords he wore, and the snug-fitting sweater, seemed to emphasise his look of the outdoors, enhancing his tan, his litheness, the power that was in every line of his body. In the pocket of his sweater was a pair of surgical scissors and a narrow flashlight used to look into ears: he must have examined a patient, then absentmindedly retained his instruments. The doctor and the man of the outdoors, two integral parts of his personality. It seemed symbolic that her last sight of him—for she knew she would not see him again—should be just like this.

'Your dance will be last,' he told her, changing the subject.

'Jenny knows?'

'Yes.' He was smiling, the blue eyes lit with a warmth that sent the adrenalin pumping fast through Sara's system. 'She's a very excited young lady today. The nurses hardly know how to cope with her.'

'I'm glad,' Sara said simply.

A hand left the wheel and closed on one of Sara's lying on her lap. She could feel the fingers against her thigh, and her heart thudded hard against her ribcage.

'You don't know how glad we all are,' Clyde said. 'The excitement seems to have given her something to live for. You'll dance for her again, Sara? After tonight?'

Sara took a deep breath. 'I'm leaving Morning Glow.'

There was an urgency in the hand that held hers. 'You're going back to Cape Town?'

'Perhaps.'

'You're going to dance professionally again?'

'I haven't decided what I'll be doing.'

'So tonight you're playing Lady Bountiful.' All the warmth had left his eyes; his voice was hard. His hand lifted from hers, abruptly, the gesture managing somehow to convey a feeling of distaste.

Angry words sprang to Sara's lips, but she stifled them before they were uttered. One retort would call forth another, and nothing would be achieved. Concealing the tears that shone in her eyes, she turned her head away. As she pretended to look through her window she wished only that the afternoon was already ended.

There was time to see Jenny after Sara had changed

into her costume and before the concert began. The little girl's face was radiant. She touched the white dress, caressed the soft folds. 'You look so beautiful,' she said rapturously. 'Mrs Burod, I've been so excited ever since Dr Clyde told me you would dance.'

'I'll be dancing specially for you,' Sara said, and was glad when Jenny was wheeled away. Her emotions were already so charged that the sight of the child's transparency, heightened even more since the last time she had seen her, threatened new tears.

The concert began. Sara could have joined the audience and watched most of it, but she chose not to. She waited for her call in a tiny room backstage. The last hour had been a drain on her emotions. She felt tense, overwrought. Now was the time to get a grip of herself. She must try not to dwell on Jenny's alarming frailness. Nor must she mourn the fact that her last time together with Clyde had turned sour just when, for once, it had been going so well.

She was called at last. As she stood in the wings, listening to the opening bars of the music, she hoped that Jenny would recall how they had read the story of *Coppélia* together, and that she would understand that the dance—the Aurora solo—had been chosen specially for her. She thought also of Clyde. Was he in the audience, and would her dancing mean anything at all to him?

And then she was dancing, giving herself to the music and the mood. Last week's stiffness was gone, and now there was only lightness, all her movements were fluid, lovely. There was joy in dancing once more, a rare joy that precluded all other emotions.

The audience was hushed. To no other act had the children given quite such attention. It was as if they sensed that they were watching something special.

The dance ended and there was a long hush. Then thunderous applause rang out, and cries of 'More, more!' Sara sank down deep in a gesture of appreciation.

'More! More!' Still the call continued.

Sara was exhilarated. She was on the stage, and her limbs were keyed with exertion, and all about her there were the smells and sounds that she knew so well. Down below in the audience people had enjoyed her dancing. Jenny was there, the little girl to whom ballet meant so much. And Clyde was there. 'More, more!' sounded the shouts, and Sara could not deny them.

A signal to the small string orchestra, then she was dancing again. The dance ended, and still the audience wanted more.

Sara was beginning to feel tired. Just for a moment the doctor's warning of so long ago flashed through her mind. And then she remembered Jenny, and the child's happiness, also the fact that she would not be dancing again after this.

She moved into the next dance, a lively, spirited one. She was spinning on one pointe when weakness struck her, and she put out a helpless hand and gave a small cry. She did not even hear the anguished moan of the audience as she collapsed.

An unfamiliar bed. White walls. A strange room, not her room at Morning Glow. Hands moving over her, strange hands, clinical. And then, as greater consciousness returned, she took in voices—two people talking. One person was Clyde, surely, though the tone was not the hard one she had grown used to. The other was strange and yet familiar too, low, professional. It came to Sara that the voice belonged to Dr Simons; he had attended her the last time she had been ill.

A door closed, and silence fell. And yet she was not alone. She sensed another presence in the room.

She wanted to open her eyes, but they felt very heavy. She tried to sit up, and fell back against the pillow. She heard an exclamation very near her, and then a hand was on her shoulders, the other supporting the back of her neck, putting her gently back against the pillow. Clyde's hands. . . . She could not mistake Clyde's hands, even if the gentleness had become unfamiliar. Again she tried to sit up.

'Lie still, my darling.'

She was dreaming. She must be dreaming. The only times she had heard Clyde talk in quite this way had been a long time ago, and after that in her dreams. In wakefulness he was hard, angry. Vaguely she remembered driving with him in a car. He had been mocking, had wanted to hurt.

A hand touched her forehead, played through her hair, pushing it very softly from her face. Lips touched her forehead.

She *was* dreaming. And yet she had the strangest feeling that she had to open her eyes. With an effort she did so, only to close them again.

'Rest, darling.'

This time her eyes opened all the way. Clyde was in the room, by her bed; she was sure of it. Before her eyes was a blur. She put all her will into making it recede, and gradually it did.

He was sitting beside her. His eyes were very blue, yet very tired. His hair was rumpled, as if a despairing hand had been thrust through it many times, and his face was taut. Sara thought he had never looked quite so strained. He was wearing clothes that she recognised, navy trousers and a matching sweater. He had worn them on the way to the concert.

The concert. . . . She had been dancing! She jerked up once more. 'I was dancing. Clyde, what happened?'

'Don't you remember?' His tone was husky, but his eyes were watchful.

'I . . . I fell. . . .'

'You collapsed. Sara, why didn't you tell me?'

Suddenly she was trembling. A hand reached for one of hers lying on top of the blanket. Clyde turned the hand palm upwards and brought the two clasped hands to lie against her cheek. She could feel the roughness of his skin.

'Tell you what?' she whispered.

'You collapsed in Cape Town. During *Swan Lake*,' he said. 'You were warned not to dance. Dr Simons told me everything.'

She could only nod.

'You let me think you didn't care about your career any more. Sara . . . Sara darling, why didn't you tell me?'

Darling—that word again. It warmed her, filled her with a wonderful happiness. Which was absurd, for it could mean nothing. Clyde had a wife.

She swallowed hard. 'At first . . . I thought you'd have seen it in the papers.'

'I was out of town at the time, and nobody told me. Don't you think I'd have come to you if I'd known?' His voice was rough. 'Later, at Morning Glow, why didn't you tell me?'

A small pink tongue came out to wet lips that were dry. 'I didn't want your pity.'

'Pity!' The word was expelled angrily. 'You've aroused many emotions in me, Sara, but pity has never been one of them.' He paused, and when he went on his tone had quietened. 'I think there's something else that needs explaining. Why did you call off our marriage?'

Her heart was beating hard against her ribcage. 'You know the reason.'

'I know what you said at the time. I want the real reason, Sara.'

She turned her gaze from his face. She had kept the truth from him for so long, it was hard to speak now. As she felt a hand cup her chin, drawing her back to look at him, she trembled.

'Clyde. . . .'

'The truth, Sara,' he said firmly.

The blue eyes held her green ones, steadily, disturbingly, defying them to shift away. Sara had no option but to speak. Slowly, a little shakily at first, she told him of the conversation she had overheard so long ago in the arbour at his parents' home in Cape Town.

'My God!' he groaned, when she had finished.

'If only I'd known! I loved you, Sara. Didn't you think I knew what was best for me? How could you have believed Belinda?'

'It . . . seemed to make sense.'

'I don't care for self-sacrificing females.' His breath fanned her cheek, and she could feel the beat of his heart strong and rhythmic against her chest as he gathered her close to him. 'But I love you. God, Sara, when I think how close I came to losing you altogether!'

'It was just a coincidence that you should have come into the Antique Den when I was there,' Sara marvelled. 'A few days earlier and Lynn would have served you.'

'Coincidence? I wonder. . . .' Clyde's eyes narrowed thoughtfully. 'I've just remembered, there was a note. . . .'

'A note?'

'From a Miss Anderson. Your Lynn, I take it?' And when Sara nodded. 'Telling me I might be interested in an antique tea-set that would be arriving a week later.'

Sara looked at him uncomprehendingly. 'I don't understand. The silver had been there two months or more.' Her eyes widened. 'Do you think Lynn meant us to meet?'

'I'd say so.'

'Why, the schemer!'

'More like a wonderful friend,' Clyde said softly. 'She must have banked on my falling in love with you all over again the moment I saw you.'

'Was she right?' Sara slanted him a radiant smile.

He drew a breath. 'Only partly, my darling.

Because you see, I'd never stopped loving you.'

He pushed her a little away from him and looked down at her. 'Don't look at me like that or I might end up making love to you in a hospital bed, and that would never do. Sara, do you know that I'll never let you go again?'

She was suddenly breathless. 'You want me to be your mistress?'

His eyes gleamed. 'Will you?'

'Yes,' she said simply, and forgot that she had agreed to a similar proposition two years earlier. And then, remembering Andrea for the first time, she clapped a hand to her mouth. 'Oh, Clyde, no, I can't. . . .'

'Why not?' She heard the bubble of laughter.

'You're married,' she said dully.

'Sara! My lovely Sara.' His voice was ragged. 'Darling, it's my turn to explain. I haven't been honest with you either. All this time you thought I was married. I did marry Andrea—not for the reasons you imagined, but because I was angry, lonely. It didn't work out. Andrea couldn't stand it any more than I could. I couldn't forget you. Sara darling, I'm divorced.'

She stared at him, eyes luminous, trying to make sense of what he was saying. 'You're not married?' she managed at last.

'I haven't been for almost a year. But I will be. I was only teasing you just now. Darling, you will marry me?'

She was trembling again. More happiness than she could grasp, but it had come too late. 'I don't know if I can have children,' she said quietly.

'I want *you*. Besides, we could adopt a child.

Jenny has been very ill, but she may have gone into remission. How would you feel about having her as a daughter?'

'Oh, Clyde, need you ask?' Green eyes were radiant. 'When can we tell her?'

'Later.' He pulled her to him once more, his lips covering her face, her throat, her ears, stirring up all the old longing. 'I love you,' he groaned.

The lips that returned to hers prevented her from telling him that she had never stopped loving him either. For a moment she struggled in his arms, then she relaxed. She would tell him later. There would be so much time to talk. All their lives, in fact.

 **ROMANCE**

Variety is the spice of romance

Each month, Mills & Boon publish new romances. New stories about people falling in love. A world of variety in romance — from the best writers in the romantic world. Choose from these titles in November.

WEDDING IN THE FAMILY   Susan Alexander
BLUE DAYS AT SEA   Anne Weale
HEARTBREAKER   Charlotte Lamb
FIRST LOVE, LAST LOVE   Carole Mortimer
TIGER MAN   Penny Jordan
DREAM HOUSE   Victoria Gordon
THE SPOTTED PLUME   Yvonne Whittal
MY DEAR INNOCENT   Lindsay Armstrong
THE JUDAS KISS   Sally Wentworth
BITTER HOMECOMING   Jan MacLean

On sale where you buy paperbacks. If you require further information or have any difficulty obtaining them, write to : Mills & Boon Reader Service, PO Box 236, Thornton Road, Croydon, Surrey CR9 3RU, England.

Mills & Boon
the rose of romance

ROMANCE

Variety is the spice of romance

Each month, Mills & Boon publish new romances. New stories about people falling in love. A world of variety in romance – from the best writers in the romantic world. Choose from these titles in October.

FLASH POINT Jane Donnelly
DANGEROUS RAPTURE Sue Peters
FALCON'S PREY Penny Jordan
NO YESTERDAYS Sheila Strutt
ANOTHER LIFE Rosemary Carter
UNTAMED WITCH Patricia Lake
SHADOWED REUNION Lillian Cheatham
DARK ENIGMA Rebecca Stratton
THE STORMS OF SPRING Sandra Field
DAUGHTER OF THE MISTY GORGES
Essie Summers

On sale where you buy paperbacks. If you require further information or have any difficulty obtaining them, write to: Mills & Boon Reader Service, PO Box 236, Thornton Road, Croydon, Surrey CR9 3RU, England.

Mills & Boon
the rose of romance